COUNTRYSIDE DAYBOOK

Compiled and Illustrated by
MARI FRIEND

PIATKUS

First published in 1991 by
Judy Piatkus (Publishers) Ltd of
5 Windmill Street, London W1P 1HF

A catalogue record for this book
is available from The British Library

ISBN 0-7499-1099-2

Produced and designed by
Savitri Books Ltd
115 J Cleveland Street
London W1P 5PN
Great Britain

Edited by Eleanor Van Zandt
Art direction and design by Mrinalini Srivastava
Typeset in Goudy Old Style by Dorchester Typesetting Ltd
Printed and bound in Hong Kong

INTRODUCTION

The illustrations in this daybook are taken from my book *Small Wonder – A New Approach to Understanding Nature*, which was written for adults who are interested in natural history, and who might like to help children to understand the world around them while learning more themselves.

The theme of *Small Wonder* revolves largely around the wildlife room of the countryside information centre which my husband, John, and I ran some years ago. Here I was able to keep bees in an observation hive, with access to the orchard outside; to raise butterflies and moths from eggs, then release them into the wildlife garden or onto the moor; and to observe the complete life cycles of many freshwater animals. Visitors to the centre were able to watch each stage in the amazing life stories of amphibians, insects and other water creatures. Adults and children alike were fascinated by the secrets revealed in the private lives of the animals. I was able to stress the responsibility we all have towards the countryside, and its plants and animals, and to pass on the sense of wonder I never cease to feel at the way these plants and animals behave in their own quiet way, and in their own good time.

The quotations I have chosen for the daybook give a flavour of the way various writers have seen the countryside during the last five hundred years. People in the past have been in awe of many plants and animals, believing them to be in some way magical or healing. Certainly there are numerous healing and beneficial plants around us, and these are once more becoming popularly used in medicine. The lore of plants and animals is another of my great interests; but in this book I have concentrated on folklore, giving an insight into some of the festivals and special days that were – and in some cases still are – celebrated in the western world. In this connection, something must be said about the calendar in use today.

Until the sixteenth century Britain and Europe observed a different calendar from the one we use today. The 'Old Style', or Julian, calendar was introduced by Julius Caesar in 46 B.C.; in this calendar, like our own, April, June, September and November had thirty days and all the other months had thirty-one, except for February, which had twenty-eight, with twenty-nine every fourth, or leap year. However, even the leap year arrangement did not result in an exact

match to the solar year, and by the sixteenth century the vernal equinox had gradually become displaced by ten days, from 21 March to 11 March. So in 1582, Pope Gregory XIII ordered ten days to be dropped from that year and ordained that in future, years ending in an even hundred would be leap years only if divisible by 400.

Non-Roman Catholic countries were very slow to accept the Gregorian edict, and held out against the 'popish' calendar for more than a century. Some German states adopted it in 1700, Britain in 1752 and Sweden in 1753. By this time the discrepancy had increased to eleven days; so the days between 2 September and 14 September of that year were missed out. This upset many people, who thought that they were losing part of their life span. The Orthodox Churches changed in the twentieth century. The Muslim calendar is lunar and has 354 days and the Jewish calendar has a solar year with twelve lunar months, an extra month being added every few years to keep the months more or less in line with the seasons.

The discrepancy between the old Julian calendar and the solar year has by now increased to thirteen days, and so the whole traditional year has 'moved forwards' by nearly two weeks. Almanacs that refer to 'Old May Day' or 'Old Christmas Day' and so on, refer to the dates on which these festivals fell in the Julian calendar. Weather predictions and advice are better suited to the old calendar, for you are more likely to find knots of may blossom on Old May Day – 13 May – than on 1 May, and it is more likely to snow on Old Christmas Day – 6 January – than on 25 December.

I hope you will enjoy this daybook and through it relive some of the celebrations of the past; but most of all, may it help you to see the need to care for the plants and animals of the countryside today.

Mari Friend

'We are part of the earth and it is part of us. The perfumed flowers are our sisters; the deer, the horse and the great eagle, these are our brothers. The rocky crests, the juices in the meadows, the body heat of the pony and man all belong to the same family.'

Chief Seattle

JANUARY

January was named after the Roman deity Janus. He was represented as a literally two-faced, bearded man, the heads being set back-to-back, one looking to the past and one to the future. Janus was the guardian of gates and doors, custodian of the universe and god of beginnings; he held sacred the first hour of the day, the first day of the month and the first month of the year.

The Monday after Twelfth Night used to be called Plough Monday. It was the day when farm work began again after the Christmas festivities, usually with spring ploughing. On this day in medieval times, real or symbolic ploughs were blessed by the parish priest.

Disturbing the Earth Mother for man's own purpose, as in ploughing, was a significant act in the lives of our ancient ancestors and had to be accompanied by suitable rituals and chants:

'Erce, Erce, good Earth Mother,
May the mighty Eternal Lord
Grant you fields to increase and flourish,
Fields fruitful and healthy,
Shining harvests of shafts of millet
And broad harvests of barley....'

Richard Jefferies (1848–87), who has been described as the 'prose poet of England's fields and hedgerows', was the author of several books and of many essays, from which the quotations contained in this daybook have been drawn.

Ploughing had a sexual significance for early man, based on the identity of woman with the earth and furrow, and of man with the plough. In Litslena, Sweden, there are some Bronze Age rock carvings that illustrate a man with an ox-team ploughing their third furrow. The ploughing of a third furrow ties in with a custom recorded in Uppland, Sweden, in the nineteenth century, in which three special furrows were ploughed on the first day of the spring sowing.

In nature, activity seems subdued by the low temperatures, but there is much to see. Tree shapes are clearly etched against the glow of a frosty sunrise or the orange of a winter sunset: branches rising, spreading their black, filigreed twigs towards the sky. The colour and texture of bark can be seen to its best advantage in the clear light of a sunny, crisp morning in winter, when the furrows, whorls and scales are clearly defined.

This is a good time of year to watch the well-camouflaged tree-creeper, spiralling his way up the trunk of a tree, exploring every crack and crevice with his slender, needle-sharp bill, searching for spiders, woodlice and tiny insects. The cheerful nuthatch has a bubbling, liquid song which rings through the stillness of a woodland. He too searches the bark, seeking out spiders and minute insects; but, unlike the treecreeper, he chooses to scuttle headfirst down the tree trunks, in an erratic, haphazard way.

'The last leaves measure our years; they are gone as the days are gone, and the bare branches silently speak of a new year, slowly advancing to its buds, its foliage and fruit.'

from *January in the Sussex Woods* by Richard Jefferies

New Year's Day. The custom of celebrating the coming of the New Year is very old. The early Romans presented one another with branches of evergreen trees at New Year; these were tokens of good luck for the coming year. It is possible that the tradition of decorating churches and houses with evergreens at this time of the year began with this ancient practice.

Twelfth Night, Epiphany, when the Three Kings, Caspar, Melchior and Balthasar, saw the infant Christ. This is the day when many people take down their Christmas decorations, as it is considered unlucky to leave them up any longer. Evergreen decorations should be burnt ceremoniously, or quietly left to rot. It was traditional to go wassailing on Twelfth Night. In this ancient custom, farmers and their workers would light bonfires in orchards and cornfields; a wassail bowl of good cheer was passed round the company, and healths were drunk to the workers, the trees and the fields. 'Wes hal' is Anglo-Saxon for 'to be of good health'.

1	*New Year's Day*
2	
3	
4	
5	*Old Christmas Eve*
6	*Old Christmas Day, now the Twelfth Day of Christmas, Feast of the Epiphany*
7	

8   JANUARY

9

10

11

12

13 *Saint Hilary's Day*
        Traditionally the coldest day of the year

14

Spanish children were brought their presents by the three Magi on the eve of the feast of the Epiphany. Naughty children were told that the Kings would bring them lumps of coal for presents, unless they mended their ways. Nowadays there is a tendency to give Christmas presents, but great processions still mark the day of the Epiphany, children eagerly awaiting the arrival of the Kings, when enormous quantities of sweets are thrown into the crowd.

Many beech and oak leaves cling to the twigs throughout the winter.

BUTTERFLIES AND FLOWERS IN JANUARY

It is too cold for butterflies to fly this month, but this is a good time to begin thinking of growing plants whose flowers will attract butterflies to your garden during the warmer days to come. Here are a few examples: achillea, cornflower, erigeron, nepeta, phlox, scabious, ice-plant, buddleia, hebe and heathers.

In sheltered places you may find the winter aconite in bloom, its yellow flowers making a pool of sunshine on the bare earth. This flower was brought from the Swiss Alps by the Celts and was a plant both loved and feared by ancient peoples. It was believed to have power against the sting of scorpions, but its poisonous juices were put on arrowheads. Imaginative people thought that a substance made from the plant's juices was used by witches, who smeared it on their bodies to enable them to fly.

The stinking hellebore may be found early in the year, the dark green leaves rising above the loose chalky or limestone slope, or from the shade of a yew tree. The flowers are nodding apple-green bells with purple rims; the seeds produced by the plant have an oily appendage (an elaiosome) which is eaten by snails; the seeds themselves adhere to the snail's slime and are thus distributed to other places where they may germinate.

Hazel catkins remain closed tightly until there is a mild spell of weather, when the male flowers expand to release pollen into the wind. The pollen is carried to the sticky, red plume-like stigmas of the female flowers growing from fat scaly 'buds' on the same, or another, tree.

The hazel was said to be the tree of knowledge, and its twigs were, and still are, used as divining rods.

NATURE IN JANUARY

Birds and mammals leave tracks in the snow, telling of their comings and goings, and of their hunting prowess – or lack of it.

During a period of prolonged cold, small birds suffer badly. If they are not able to bathe, their feathers stick together and can no longer be puffed up to insulate them from the frost.

In Finland 75 per cent of goldcrests are reckoned to die during a normal winter, and 85 per cent during a very cold one. Goldcrests feed on insects and their pupae and eggs, found in cracks in tree bark, or in the crevices of cones. Winter losses are made good in the breeding season, when the tiny birds produce ten or eleven eggs in each clutch.

Red and grey squirrels are preparing to have their first litters.

A mole's country name is 'mouldewarp', or earth thrower. A thaw in January will bring with it a rash of molehills: earth that has been excavated from tunnels worked just below the ground's surface. In winter, in fens or low-lying land, you may find a large molehill; this is a fortress in which the mole has a dry nest and a store of insects and worms.

Watch the birds in the garden and the park; you may see pair formations of dunnocks, wrens, robins and ducks.

Crossbills begin breeding early in the year, when their main foods, larch, pine and spruce seeds, are mature. These birds also eat the seeds of ivy, rowan, hawthorn, weeds, grasses and thistles, as well as flies and beetles.

Badger cubs are born between mid-January and mid-March, in a lined breeding chamber where they remain for about eight weeks. On mild breezy days, the parent badgers bring the bedding outside to be aired.

Otters enjoy sliding in deep snow, in icy conditions.

Starlings begin to develop colour flashes at the base of their bills: pink if female and blue if male.

Red foxes are especially noisy in winter, the mating season, when the chilling barks and screams of the fox's serenade to a prospective mate echo around the countryside.

Long-tailed field mice enjoy eating bulbs at this hungry time of the year.

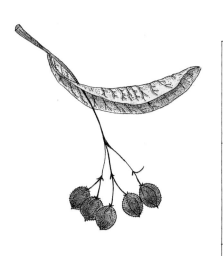

15	
16	
17	*Old Twelfth Night*

Plough Monday falls on the
first Monday after Twelfth
Night.

18	

The third Monday in
January is observed in the
United States as the
birthday of Martin Luther
King (1929–68), the
revered black civil rights
leader.

19	
20	*Eve of Saint Agnes's Day* *The sun enters the House of Aquarius*
21	*Saint Agnes's Day*

22   JANUARY

23

24

25   *Burns Night*

Robert Burns, the poet was
born on 25 January 1759.
Scots everywhere celebrate
by holding Burns suppers, in
which the main item on the
menu is haggis.

26

27

28

Some 135 years ago the Suwamish Indians in the northwestern territories of the United States were fighting for their very survival. The white men eventually forced them into a reservation in 1855. Their chief, by the name of Seattle, made some statements that were ignored at the time, but the depth of his vision and understanding have now acquired a chilling significance:

'Man treats his mother, the earth, and his brother, the sky, as things to be bought, plundered, sold like sheep or bright beads. His appetite will devour the earth and leave behind only a desert.'

Chief Seattle

'Jan. 3rd. 1771. Wood lice, *Oniscus asellus*, appear all the winter in mild weather: spiders appear all the winter in moist weather; *Lepismae* [silver fish and fire brats] appear all the winter round hearths and in warm places. Some kinds of gnats appear all the winter in mild weather, as do earthworms, after it is dark, when there is no frost.'

Gilbert White

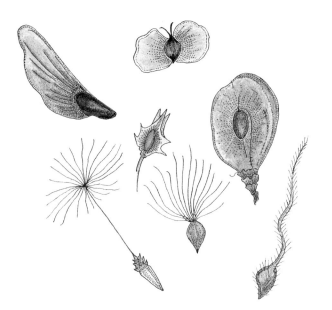

Gilbert White (1720–93) was born in Selborne, in Hampshire, where he spent most of his life. In 1751 he began to keep a 'Naturalist's Journal', which reveals his affectionate and detailed observations of wildlife and nature. It formed the basis of his Natural History and Antiquities of Selborne, *which remains a classic.*

29	JANUARY
30	
31	

'The walls of the palace were formed of the drifting snow, and the windows and doors of the cutting winds. There were more than a hundred halls, all blown together by the snow: the greatest of these extended for several miles; the strong Northern Light illuminated them all. How great and empty they were, and how icily cold and shining! Never was merriment there, not even a little bear's ball, at which the storm could have played the music:…'

from *The Snow Queen*, by Hans Christian Andersen
(1805–75)

'One for sorrow, Two for mirth,
Three for a wedding, Four for a birth,
Five for the rich, Six for the poor,
Seven for a witch, Eight for one more;
Nine for a burying, Ten for a dance,
Eleven for England, Twelve for France.'

Magpies, an old rhyme

FEBRUARY

The month of February gets its name from the Latin *februare*, 'to cleanse', after the ancient Roman festival of fertility and purification, Lupercalia. On 15 February the priests of Lupercus, the fertility god, would assemble at his cave, where they sacrificed goats. The shedding of this blood was thought to purify the land for the new year. It is believed that King Numa Pompilius (reigned c. 715–673 B.C.) named the month after this purification.

Lupercus is often associated with another Roman nature god, Faunus, who in turn is identified with the Greek god Pan, the deity of shepherds and flocks.

Pan had the feet, horns and tail of a goat, and he hunted and danced around the countryside in the company of beautiful nymphs. He would play tricks on travellers by hiding in the forest and suddenly jumping out with a shout, filling the startled mortals with 'panic'. Pan loved many nymphs, including one called Syrinx, but she ran from him in terror and was changed into a reed. Pan, who had a love of music, plucked the reed and made a syrinx – Pan's pipe – on which to play, so keeping the nymph with him forever.

Despite the furry coats of mammals and the layered feathers of birds, the biting cold is difficult to keep at bay. To save themselves from freezing, animals must use their reserves of fat to generate warmth. It is hard to find food in cold weather, and the used fat is very difficult to replace. It is even more difficult to survive if the weather is wet as well as cold, for damp fur and feathers do not keep the body heat in.

Where snow falls in February, the warm sun penetrates the snow layer and heats the ground. The layer of snow next to the earth melts and a space is formed; voles and mice are able to live in these corridors beneath the snow. Here they feed on roots and plants that are not frozen, and they are safe from owls and kestrels. Rabbits and deer dig away the snow in order to feed on the soft vegetation below.

Despite the gloom of this month, the frost which continues to harden the ground and the snow which piles in drifts, there is a tingle in the air. A little tingle that thrills down every twig, through every bird's feather and through the cold, wet earth; it is February, and soon, very soon, the sun will shine with renewed strength and it will be spring.

Folklore relating to the weather in February stresses the idea that a mild February is an ill omen, with bad weather sure to follow.

'As many fogs in February,
So many frosts in May.
    If the sun shines on Candlemas Day
    Snow will fall on May Day.'

'I leant upon a coppice gate
When Frost was spectre-gray,
And Winter's dregs made desolate
The weakening eye of day.
The tangled bine-stems scored the sky
Like strings from broken lyres,
And all mankind that haunted nigh
Had sought their household fires.'

from *The Darkling Thrush*
by Thomas Hardy (1840–1928)

An evergreen: the holm oak

It was believed that the trees threw off their winter sleep on 24 February, Saint Matthias's Day. It is a day on which to look forward to spring and the promise of better times.

Candlemas Day on 2 February heralds the season when winter's grip begins to relax and the days noticeably lengthen.

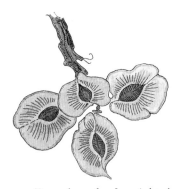

Forty days after Jesus's birth, the Virgin Mary ritually cleansed herself and presented her baby in the Temple of Jerusalem. It is there that Simeon prophesied that Jesus would be a 'light to lighten the Gentiles'.

1 *Saint Bride's Day, the patron saint of midwives and pregnant women*
Imbolc, the Celtic feast of spring's awakening

2 *Candlemas Day*
Saint Mary's feast of the candles

3

4

5 *Saint Agatha's Day, the patron saint of bakers and bellfounders*

6

7

9   *Saint Apollonia's Day, the patron saint of dentists*

10

11

12   *Abraham Lincoln's birthday (1809–65)*

13

14   *Saint Valentine's Day*

Saint Valentine was a Christian martyr of the third century, whose feast day, the 14th, replaced the old Roman feast of Lupercalia. Legend says that Claudius, Emperor of Rome, issued a decree forbidding marriage, as married men did not want to leave their families and go to war. The priest, Valentine, invited young lovers to come to him and be married in secret; when Claudius found out he had Valentine thrown into prison where he died.

BUTTERFLIES IN FEBRUARY

In years when February is mild, brimstone butterflies wake up from hibernation. Before the word 'butterfly' was coined, these beautiful insects were known as 'coloured-flies'. The early flying brimstone butterfly was eagerly looked for as a sign of spring, and because it has butter-coloured wings, it was referred to as 'butter-fly'. Gradually the word 'butterfly' came to embrace all species, and the brimstone acquired its present name, which relates to the colour of sulphur.

WILDFLOWERS IN FEBRUARY

Snowdrop, dog's mercury, common alder, aspen, coltsfoot, mistletoe.

'And what is there to life if a man cannot hear the lonely cry of the whippoorwill, or the argument of the frogs around a pond at night?'

Chief Seattle

'In ancient times, a young man studying at a forest ashram was asked by his guru to find a single plant or tree which was useless to mankind. After years of research, the student returned to concede to his guru that such a plant or tree did not exist. In the meantime he had learned the secrets held within the leaves, flowers, fruit and bark of the myriad plants of the country. The young man became an acknowledged authority in the ancient Indian system of medicine.'

ancient Hindu lore

NATURE IN FEBRUARY

Cock pheasants look magnificent as they strut across the snow, gold-burnished plumage, scarlet wattles, and blue head shimmering.

Lapwings gather in flocks to feed on farmland and seashore mud flats. They feed by taking a short run, pausing to tilt forward to peck and then running again.

Look for waxwings feeding on berried shrubs. As food stocks diminish, the birds will often feed from cotoneaster and pyracantha bushes in parks and gardens.

Nest boxes begin to be claimed, so make sure you have cleaned out the nesting materials from last year.

Winter moths may be seen flying in car headlights. The flightless females await the males, sitting on the trunks of apple and other fruit trees.

On the hedgebank the first young leaves of cow parsley and the bright, ivy-shaped leaves of lesser celandine are pushing through.

Stoats may be seen, hunting around rabbit holes and climbing trees for squirrels and roosting birds. Stoats sometimes 'dance' to put birds off their guard, jumping and twisting for some minutes before suddenly leaping on their audience.

Velvet shanks are yellow-brown winter fungi; they sprout in bunches from tree trunks. The winter polypore is another winter toadstool; this grows on tree stumps and fallen branches.

Green woodpeckers call with a shrill laugh. Their numbers suffer in winter frosts, for although they eat wood-boring insects, beetles, flies and moths, they much prefer ants and their larvae, which are not available at this time.

Yüan Tan, the Chinese New Year, is a two-week-long festival occurring between late January and late February, varying with the Chinese calendar. The observances begin with cleaning one's house and putting on new clothes, to symbolize a fresh start, and culminate with the Lantern Festival, at the new moon, when there are noisy and colourful processions in the streets, dominated by a ferocious 'lion' who dances to the sound of gong, drums and firecrackers.

15

16

17

18

19

20 *The sun enters the House of Pisces*

21

22 *Saint Matthew's Day*	**FEBRUARY**

23

24 *Saint Matthias's Day, the patron saint of carpenters and woodcutters*

25

26

27

28–29 *Leap Year's Day*

George Washington (1732–99) was the first President of the United States. He distinguished himself as a soldier and was chosen to be the Commander in Chief during the American War of Independence. His birthday is now observed on the third Monday in February.

Leap Year's Day occurs only once every four years. On this day, ladies have absolute licence to propose marriage to single gentlemen. Should the proposal be refused, the gentleman is bound to give the lady a present – usually a pair of gloves.

The hawthorn is a tree of hedgerows, woodland edges and glades, where it can grow to about 12 metres (40 feet) in height. About one hundred and fifty insects are associated with the hawthorn, but fortunately they will also visit other plants in the family Rosaceae.

Long ago, hawthorn was considered to be a tree of magic and mystery, supernaturally powerful at all times against witchcraft, fairy mischief and lightning. This belief helped to make it a popular plant for protective hedges and for walking sticks. There is, however, a certain fickleness about the magic of some plants, and hawthorn is one of them; for, although it is good to have hawthorn trees around your home and to fasten boughs of hawthorn over your door, it is considered extremely unlucky to take the flowers of the hawthorn inside your house. To do so will bring bad luck or even death to a member of the family. For this reason some people still call the hawthorn 'mother die'.

There is a key to this picture at the back of the book.

Within a thick and spreading hawthorn bush
That overhung a molehill large and round,
I heard from morn to morn a merry thrush
Sing hymns to sunrise, and I drank the sound
With joy; and often, an intruding guest,
I watched her secret toil from day to day.
How true she warped the moss, to form a nest,
And modelled it within with wood and clay;
And by and by, like heath bells gilt with dew,
There lay her shining eggs, as bright as flowers,
Ink spotted over shells of greeny blue;
And there I witnessed in the sunny hours
A brood of Nature's minstrels chirp and fly,
Glad as the sunshine and the laughing sky.

The Thrush's Nest by John Clare
(1793–1864)

MARCH

March was named after Mars, the Roman god of war. It is the month that sees the end of winter and the beginning of spring.

Norsemen thought of March as 'the lengthening month that wakes the alder and blooms the whin [gorse]'. It was known by the name 'Lencten', meaning 'spring', and because the winter stores were very low at this time, it was a period of enforced fasting. 'Lencten' was adopted by the early Church and called Lent, most of which falls during March.

The day before the beginning of Lent (in February) is known as Shrove Tuesday, or by its French name, Mardi Gras. In some countries colourful carnivals lasting a week or more are held before Mardi Gras itself.

On the day before the Lenten fast, Christians of medieval times and earlier made their pre-Lent confessions or shrifts – 'shrift' is the word from which Shrove Tuesday took its name. After their confessions, the congregation took their last opportunity of eating any 'luxury' food they still possessed, before the Lenten prohibition. So all the eggs and the fat in the house were made into pancakes, hence the festival's nickname of 'Pancake Day'.

On the first day of Lent, Ash Wednesday, it is traditional in the Roman Catholic Church, and among some Anglicans, to mark worshippers' foreheads with ashes (the burnt palm branches of the previous year's Palm Sunday) as a sign of penitence.

Although spring officially begins in March, the weather may still be wintry. Yet, despite the cold winds, frosts, snow showers and rain, the sun's rays are warmer and there is a change in the air, a feeling of excitement runs through the land.

Pollen from the yew and hazel drifts in the wind – living motes of procreation, tiny grains which carry the germs of future trees. There is a pale green tinge along the hedgerows, where hawthorn leaves are breaking from their encapsulating buds and unfurling in a welcome haze. Silvery-grey, rabbit-soft sallow catkins unfold; coltsfoot and celandine reflect the sun in patches of gold on waste ground and on hedge bank, while wood anemones open their pale, starry flowers in shaded places.

On calm, sunny days the first insects appear; honey bees happy to leave the hive after their long confinement; bumble bee queens, awake from hibernation, feed on the nectar and pollen offered by the sallow catkins before zigzagging low over the ground, searching for nesting places, in old mouse or vole holes, or under piles of vegetation. Early butterflies flex their stiff wing muscles in the sunshine, and birds sing out their territorial songs; all life begins to stir in the springtime of the year.

'The rains have come, and frogs are full of glee.
They sing in chorus, with voices loud and lusty.
They sing in primeval joy:
There is nothing to fear today, neither hunger nor death…
In the sensual rain there is ecstasy of touch,
How luscious is the mud, how young, how soft!…
It is midnight. We have closed our doors and are warm in bed.
And the stillness is broken by a single tireless voice.
It is the final stanza of the mystic chanting.
The croak, croak, croak of the last lonely frog.'

from *Frogs* by Buddhadeva Bose, (1908–)
translated from Bengali

Saint David's Day. Legend has it that the Welsh victory over the Saxons in A.D. 640 was made possible because the Welsh fastened leeks on their tunics in order to recognize each other, while the Saxons, who did not wear badges, spent much of the time battling with each other. On this, the Welsh National Day, many people in Wales wear a leek.

1   *Saint David's Day, patron saint of Wales*

2

3

4

5

6

7

8 MARCH

9

10

11

12

13

14

BUTTERFLIES IN MARCH

Brimstone, speckled wood, green hairstreak, small tortoiseshell.

WILDFLOWERS IN MARCH

Primrose, wych elm, opposite-leaved golden saxifrage, butterbur, white violet, hairy violet, lesser celandine, goat willow, marsh marigold, barren strawberry, wood anemone.

'A windy March foretells a fine May.'

'March 26th 1773. Grass begins to grow. A large flock of titlarks on the common, feeding and flitting on, probably going down to the forest to the moory, moist places.

Gilbert White

'Seldom do we realize that the world is practically no thicker to us than the print of our footsteps on the path. Upon that surface we walk and act our comedy of life, and what is underneath is nothing to us. But it is out from that under-world, from the dead and the unknown, from the cold moist ground, that these green blades have sprung.'

from *Out of Doors in February* by Richard Jefferies

'The air is precious to the red man, for all things share the same breath – the beast, the tree and the human. The white man does not seem to notice the air he breathes.'

Chief Seattle

NATURE IN MARCH

Bright, pollen-laden male catkins open on the goat willow before the leaves begin to unfurl. Female catkins are borne on separate trees; these are not so visually attractive to us, but their tiny nectaries invite bumble bees, honey bees and hover flies.

Nest building begins in earnest this month. Hang up a net of wool, moss, feathers and bits of string, and watch the birds collect their building materials.

Shrews, voles and mice all come into breeding condition. Lay corrugated iron sheets over areas of rough grass so that, later on, you will be able to see the runs and nests made underneath.

This is the month to watch for 'mad March hares'. They rear up on their back legs and 'box' with their front paws as they flirt and compete in the fields.

Lapwings call and display to each other in fluid, aerobatic movements. Should a predator appear near the nest, it will be lured away with an 'injured-wing' display.

Frogs are now active, clamped together in ponds. Toads will breed in the same pond, but they prefer deeper water with more weed. Look for toads in a mild spell, when there has been some rain during the afternoon or evening. Their spring migrations to spawning grounds usually take place at night.

Tawny owls call hauntingly across chilly night skies, while in the forests of the north, the secretive long-eared owl groans plaintively.

Golden daffodils open in many gardens. Their country name of daffydowndilly is often shortened to 'daffy', a name which resembles 'Dafydd' or 'Taffy', a nickname given to Welsh people. This is perhaps why some Welsh patriots wear a daffodil rather than a leek on Saint David's Day; or maybe because they smell so much sweeter!

In Shakespeare's *Julius Caesar*, a soothsayer cautioned Caesar to 'beware the Ides of March' – correctly, as it turned out, for he was assassinated on that day. In the ancient Roman calendar, the Ides were the fifteenth day of March, May, July and October and the thirteenth day of the other months.

Saint Patrick's Day. Saint Patrick illustrated the doctrine of the Trinity to the Irish people by using a plant with trifoliate leaves, a shamrock. So the Irish wear a shamrock on this day – often a clover, such as the lesser clover. There are parades, pageants, fun and feasting.

15	
16	
17	*Saint Patrick's Day, patron saint of Ireland*
18	
19	*Saint Joseph's Day*
20	
21	*Spring equinox, the first day of spring. The sun enters the House of Aries*

22

23

24 *Saint Gabriel's Day, patron saint of postmen and messengers*

25 *Lady Day, the Feast of the Annunciation*

Lady Day commemorates the day that the Archangel Gabriel told the Virgin Mary that she would bear the Christ Child nine months later.

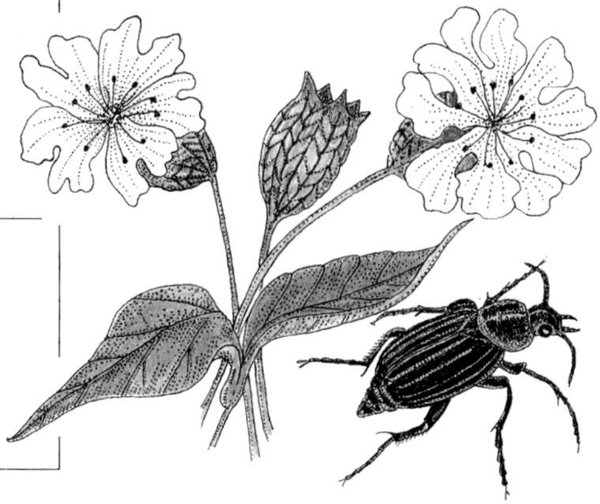

26

27

28

'I am a wind on the sea,
I am a wave of the ocean,
I am the roar of the sea,
I am a powerful ox,
I am a hawk on a cliff.'

from *Amergin's*
Chant Book of Invasions

Honey bees are considered to be very intelligent insects. They should never be killed, nor should they be sold, for a bought swarm never thrives. You can, however, exchange bees for goods. If you have a hive of bees, you must always tell them if someone in the family dies, gets married or has a baby. If you don't tell the bees they will desert the hive; if they continue to hum contentedly when you have told them the news, then they have accepted it.

'Be sure that you talk to the bees,' he said,
With a puff on his pipe and a shake of his head.
'For should someone come or should someone go,
Then it's right that the bees should be told, you know.

'When I was a lad and the master died,
I took over the bees and the land beside,
And I told them then that my name was John,
And they'd work for me from that day on.

'Births and deaths and weddings as well,
These are the things it's the custom to tell.
And it's no use asking me why it's so,
But it's proper and right that the bees must know.

'Be sure to talk to the bees,' he said
With a puff on his pipe and a shake of his head.
He was wrinkled and grey but it's certainly sure,
I shall always remember his strange country lore.

Anon

29	MARCH
30	
31	

The Jewish feast of Purim normally falls in March, sometimes in February. It commemorates the escape of Persian Jews from a massacre in the fifth century B.C., thanks to the intervention of Queen Esther. Observances include readings from the Book of Esther, feasting and the giving of presents.

'Between the barn and the stream the ground was overgrown with rank weeds, and here one day Caleb came by chance upon his cat eating something among the weeds – a good-sized fresh-caught trout! On examining the ground he found it littered with the heads, fins and portions of backbones of the trout their cat had been feeding on every day since they had been in possession of him. They did not destroy their favourite, nor tell anyone of their discovery, but they watched him and found that it was his habit to bring a trout every day to that spot, but how he caught his fish was never known.'

from *The Illustrated Shepherd's Life*
by William Henry Hudson (1841–1922)

APRIL

April is from the Roman Aperilis; *aperio* means to open or display. This is when we begin to see the blossoming of spring, the tentative opening of leaves and flowers which culminates in the most welcome display of the year.

Primroses dapple woodlands with their pale moon-yellow clusters; shy dog violets glow, rose-pink herb-Robert and milky-white greater stitchwort gleam silkily; purple-blue ground-ivy and delicate blush-white wood-sorrel carpet the warming earth. Orange-tip butterflies flit from lady's smock to garlic mustard and on to dame's violet, carefully choosing the plants on which to lay their eggs.

Spring is the best time to see the different layers of vegetation that create a woodland. The branches and leaves of fully grown trees form the overall canopy of the tree layer. Below this are the shrubs and small trees of the shrub layer, and on the floor of the wood is the carpeting field layer of herbaceous plants, ferns and mosses. The trees of beech woods and coniferous plantations often exclude so much light that they have little or no shrub and field layers, so many birds are prevented from nesting in these areas.

During late March and early April, frogs and toads make their annual pilgrimage to water in order to mate and lay their eggs. Each female is beset by many eager suitors and often has several males clinging to her rapturously; for the ability of a male to hold tight and ultimately shed his sperm over the female's eggs ensures the continuity of his own family line.

In pagan times the rebirth of nature was celebrated by honouring the goddess of spring, Eostra. Centuries later, Christian priests put the emphasis on the rebirth of mankind, a celebration of the Resurrection of Christ from the dead; they called the feast Easter. However, the Church failed to stop people from climbing to the hilltops in order to see the sun rise, then dance for joy at its appearance in the eastern sky.

The Resurrection took place during the Jewish festival of Passover, and because the date of Passover is variable – it is dependent on the phases of the moon – Easter, too, is a movable feast.

Easter is a very important feast in the Christian year, and there are many popular customs associated with it, some of which probably date back to medieval times. Cross buns, or hot cross buns as they are usually called, are a traditional Easter treat. They are baked with a cross slashed into their tops, and in some places in the north of England they are oval-shaped. Eggs have long been a symbol of life and fertility, and the Christian Church adopted the symbolism; so the hatching chick was said to be symbolic of Christ's Resurrection. Chocolate eggs also reflect this symbolism. Certainly an egg, a seed of life, gives the idea of continuity, be it of gods or of the seasons; and we surely know that spring has arrived once again.

Passover, or the Feast of Unleavened Bread, is an important Jewish festival, normally falling in April; it commemorates the Exodus of the Hebrews from Egypt in the thirteenth century B.C. The six-day festival begins with a special meal, called the Seder, at which the story is re-told.

All Fools' Day; in France, *poisson d'avril*. The origin of this day is much disputed. It is a day when practical jokes are played on friends, sending them on fools' errands, or tricking them into doing ludicrous things. It is for this reason that some believe All Fools' Day to have started with Noah, who sent a dove out of the ark before the waters had abated – on a fool's errand. In France the 'fool' has a paper fish pinned on his, or her, back.

1 *All Fools' Day or April Fools' Day*

2

3

4

5

6 *Lady Day Old Style*

7

8

9

10

11

12

13

14

It is traditional for parents to give small children an 'Easter basket', filled with coloured hard-boiled eggs, chocolate eggs and other sweets. The basket, supposedly brought by the Easter Bunny, is left on the doorstep or hidden in the house for the child to discover on Easter morning.

BUTTERFLIES IN APRIL

Large white, small white, green-veined white, Duke of Burgundy fritillary, holly blue, common blue, map butterfly, orange tip, painted lady, swallowtail, brimstone, speckled wood, green hairstreak, small tortoiseshell.

WILDFLOWERS IN APRIL

Meadow saxifrage, blackthorn, dandelion, cuckoo flower or lady's smock, ramsons or wild garlic, cowslip, bluebell, ash, silver birch, wood sorrel, greater stitchwort, cow parsley, field forget-me-not, lords and ladies or cuckoo pint, early purple orchid, meadow buttercup.

It is lucky to be walking when you hear the first cuckoo, and sitting down when you see the first swallow.

Spring has come when you can put your foot on three daisies at once.

'...amongst the beautiful green grass, grew a little daisy. The sun shone as warmly and as brightly upon it as on the great splendid garden flowers, and so it grew from hour to hour. One morning it stood in full bloom, with its little shining white petals spreading like rays round the little yellow sun in the centre. It never thought that no man would notice it down in the grass, and that it was a poor despised little flower; no, it was very merry, and turned to the warm sun, looked up to it, and listened to the lark carolling high in the air.'

From *The Daisy* by Hans Christian Andersen

NATURE IN APRIL

The garden pond is an important refuge for frogs and toads, and even a small pond can also attract the secretive newt to its watery depths.

More and more butterflies and moths are to be seen, especially on sunny days.

Stoats and weasels will be having their first litters over the next few weeks. This coincides with the peak breeding time for other small mammals and birds.

Noctule bats gather in excited groups to hunt over ponds and lakes where flying insects are ascending from the water.

The first baby squirrels are venturing out of their nurseries, while their parents are courting again. This will probably give rise to further litters in June or early July.

Badger and red fox cubs come out of their underground nurseries to play around their mother.

Bee-flies can be seen hovering around flowers. The insect has a brown, furry, bee-like body, but its fast, erratic flight tells you that this is not a true bee. Look for the long, slender proboscis with which it sips nectar from flowers.

Look out for the Saint George's mushroom in rough grassland; it has a thick, white, fleshy cap and stem.

As the soil and leaf litter warm up, many insects are busy on the surface of the ground.

Nightingales, cuckoos, swallows, house martins and many other birds now return from Africa.

Orchards bloom; *hanafubuki*, the Japanese word for orchard, means 'flowering snowstorm'.

15

16

17

18

19

20

21 *The sun enters the House of Taurus*

22

23 *Saint George's Day, the patron saint of England*

24 *Saint Mark's Eve*

Saint Mark's Eve. In bygone days this was a time for divination of future love, for performing various magical actions before going to bed to dream of one's future husband. So shoes were put by the bed, one coming and one going, with garters hanging above them; the young girl stripped with her back to the bed and walked backwards to it. Many bits of 'magic' of this kind were enacted.

25 *Saint Mark's Day*

It was also a ghostly time, when, it was said, one could sit in the church porch at midnight and see the shrouded ghosts of those who would die in the coming year, passing into church.

26

27

28

| 30 | *May Eve, the Eve of Beltane, the Celtic festival of summer's beginning* |

'The rivers are our brothers, they quench our thirst. The rivers carry our canoes and feed our children. If we sell you our land, you must remember, and teach your children, that the rivers are our brothers and yours, and you must henceforth give the rivers the kindness you would give to a brother.'

Chief Seattle

'The swallows bring us the sunbeams on their wings from Africa to fill the fields with flowers. From the time of the arrival of the first swallow the flowers take heart; the few and scanty plants that had braved the earlier cold are succeeded by a constantly enlarging list, till the banks and lanes are full of them.'

from *Nature on the Roof* by Richard Jefferies

'April 9th 1774. The ring-ouzel appears on its spring migration. It feeds now on ivy berries, which just begin to ripen. Ivy blossoms in October. In the autumn it feeds on haws, yew berries and also on worms.'

Gilbert White

Be sure to put a crust of salted bread under your baby's pillow on May Eve, to keep witches away.

MAY

May is named for Maia, the beautiful daughter of Atlas and Pleione, who was loved by Zeus, the father of the gods, and who gave him a son, Hermes. Maia was identified by the Romans as a goddess of spring.

The face of the countryside changes rapidly during May; this is a month combining the freshness of April and the warmth of June. May is a musical month, when birdsong reaches its climax, streams gurgle, bees hum and a sea of bluebells drifts beneath the trees.

Orchards bloom with billowing clouds of creamy white and pastel-pink blossoms busy with bees, while bullfinches pull at the flower buds in a rain of pale petals. Tender leaves unfurl, lime green and red-bronze, translucent in the sunshine; horse chestnuts bear their pink and white 'candle' flowers among their leaves, ready to light up the trees with their beauty at the end of the month. Then there is the may, the flower of the month, covering every hawthorn with white and insect-laden loveliness.

'There is no quiet place in the white man's cities; no place to hear the unfurling of leaves in the spring, or the rustle of the insect's wings.'

Chief Seattle

'When daisies pied and violets blue,
And lady-smocks all silver-white,
And cuckoo buds of yellow hue
Do paint the meadows with delight.
The cuckoo then on every tree,
Mocks married men; for thus sings he,
Cuckoo.'

from *Love's Labour's Lost*
by William Shakespeare (1564–1616)

May Day is the great festival of the coming of summer.
Philip Stubbes, a sixteenth-century Puritan writer, was dismayed by the pagan festival; he wrote disapprovingly of the 'chiefest jewel', the maypole, being brought home with great veneration by twenty or forty yoke of oxen, every ox having a nosegay of flowers on its horns. He described the maypole being covered over with flowers and herbs all bound about with ribbons and sometimes brightly painted. The pole was erected with handkerchiefs and flags at the top and straw around the bottom, on which the people danced.

The May Day festival in fact replaced the full-blooded pagan rite of Beltane, when our ancient ancestors drove their flocks and herds between two fires to purify them, before setting them loose to graze the pastures until Hallowe'en. On May Day Eve, the fires were set on hilltops, and the wood burnt was from nine different trees; the people danced sun-wise, from east to west, around the leaping flames in an orgiastic rite, engaging in the act of mass union between the sexes that was performed by primitive peoples all over the world.

To bathe one's face in dew just before sunrise on May morning is to ensure a beautiful complexion.

May Day is still celebrated by dancing and merrymaking in some places. The maypole around which young people dance is probably a relic of our tree-worshipping past. It is certainly a form of nature worship, the people in ecstasy at the passing of winter and the coming of spring.

In Scandinavia, in the old days, people welcomed May with mock battles between characters representing summer and winter, in which summer always won.

Rood Day, or Cross-mass Day, was traditionally a day for taking the cow to the bull.

Ascension Day celebrates Christ's ascension into Heaven. This day is also known as Holy Thursday and occurs on the fortieth day after Easter.

1	*May Day*
2	*Rood Day, or Cross-mass*
3	
4	
5	
6	
7	

9

10

11

12   *Saint Pancras's Day*

13   *Old May Day*

14

Saint Pancras was a Roman boy who was martyred at the age of fourteen. He is one of the patron saints of children and is also invoked against headaches.

On Old May Day, Morris dancers would tie thirty or forty bells around their legs and take colourful handkerchiefs in their hands; their pipers would pipe and their drummers thunder, while the dancers leaped and skipped, causing their bells to jangle. Hobbyhorses and sometimes other monsters would skirmish among the people.

BUTTERFLIES IN MAY

Large white, small white, green-veined white, Duke of Burgundy fritillary, holly blue, common blue, map butterfly, orange-tip, painted lady, swallowtail, brimstone, speckled wood, small tortoiseshell, green hairstreak, wood white, white admiral, red admiral, heath fritillary, wall brown, large blue, small heath, peacock.

WILDFLOWERS IN MAY

Horse-chestnut, hawthorn, tormentil, red campion, creeping buttercup, yellow pimpernel, holly, wild pansy, common comfrey, garlic mustard, herb-Robert, lesser spearwort, bugle, brooklime, ox-eye daisy, scarlet pimpernel.

Hawthorn was used to decorate doorways on May Day to keep evil spirits away. To take it inside was a sure sign of the impending death of someone in the house, and hawthorn is often known as 'mother-die'.

The rhyme 'Here we go gathering nuts in May' is thought to have its origins in the song sung by young men gathering knots of may blossom for the May Day celebrations.

It is unlucky to buy or use a new broom, or brush, this month; for it is said, 'Sweep with a broom that is cut in May, you'll sweep the head of the house away.'

NATURE IN MAY

Queen wasps are searching for nest sites. When you hear them rasping on wood they have started to build their wasp paper nests.

Pipistrelle bats fly from their roost at dusk. Watch for the larger Daubenton's bats skimming the surface of lakes or ponds, feeding on mayflies as they emerge from the water.

Ladybirds begin mating and laying their shiny eggs close to colonies of aphids, on which they feed.

Grass-snakes enjoy the warmth of a compost heap. You may be lucky enough to find a clutch of up to forty parchment-shelled eggs; leave them to incubate for six to ten weeks. The little snakes will emerge and disperse to a damp habitat.

Orange-tip butterflies are feeding; they lay their eggs on cuckoo-flower, hedge mustard, honesty and dame's violet.

Badger cubs go out with their parents to learn the art of hunting invertebrates, such as earthworms and insects.

Wood ants begin to be very active – dashing to and fro, industriously carrying leaves and twigs to incorporate into their nests.

Mining bees are busy digging their nest burrows in sandy soil; leaf-cutter bees line ready-made holes with pieces of leaf, neatly cut from rose bushes; wool-carder bees upholster holes with down shaved from the leaves of verbascum and stachys; while mason bees build a tiny cell of earth mixed with saliva in crevices in walls.

This is a good month to plant herbs, which will enhance your cooking and make the garden attractive to insects. Chives, rosemary and hyssop attract many insects; the large blue flowers of sage are particularly inviting to bumble bees; thyme is a butterfly attractor; and fennel brings in the hover flies.

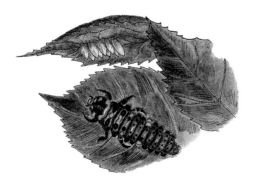

Rogationtide covers Ascension Day and the preceding two days. At this time there is a long established custom of 'beating the bounds' by ceremonially walking around parish boundaries; a cross or banner is sometimes carried at the front of the procession and the crops may be blessed along the route.

15

16

17

18

19

20

21

22 *The sun enters the House of Gemini*   **MAY**

23

24

25

26

27

28

Whitsunday falls on the
seventh Sunday after
Easter. Whitsuntide is the
English name for the Feast
of the Pentecost, when the
Holy Spirit descended on
the Apostles, filling them
with the knowledge of the
work they had to do.

'I take it for granted that you have been in the country, and seen a very old farm-house with a thatched roof, and mosses and small plants growing wild upon the thatch. There is a stork's nest on the top of the gable; for we can't do without the stork. The walls of the house are sloping, and the windows are low, and only one of the latter is made so it will open. The baking-oven sticks out of the wall like a little fat body. The elder tree hangs over the fence, and beneath its branches, at the foot of the fence, is a pool of water in which a few ducks are enjoying themselves.'

from *What the Old Man Does Is Always Right*
by Hans Christian Andersen

'The orange-golden dandelion in the sward was deeply laden with colour brought to it anew again and again by the ships of the flowers, the humble bees – to their quays they come, unlading priceless essences of sweet odours brought from the East over the green seas of wheat, unlading priceless colours on the broad dandelion disks, bartering these things for honey and pollen.

from *Wild Flowers* by Richard Jefferies

'May 9th 1793. The magpies which probably have young, are now very ravenous and destroy the broods of missel thrushes, tho' the dams are fierce birds, and fight boldly in defence of their nests.'

Gilbert White

It is said that cats born in May are unlucky and incapable of catching mice and rats!

29 *Oak-Apple Day in England*	**MAY**
30	
31	

May 29 – Oak-Apple Day. The day that Charles II entered London and was restored to the throne, thereby ending the Cromwellian rule. Charles had hidden from the Roundheads in an oak tree after his defeat at Worcester, so Royalists wore oak sprigs to commemorate this. They were probably unaware that they were also perpetuating a pagan festival honouring the most sacred of trees.

Red and white campion are visited by butterflies, moths, long-tongued bees, hover flies.

JUNE

June, the queen of months, is said to be named for Juno, wife of Jupiter in Roman mythology. Like the Greek goddess Hera, Juno was the protectress of women and childbirth, and goddess of the moon.

June is a radiant month of long days, of intense animal activity, of a profusion of flowers and plants in full maturity. June is the month of rambling, scrambling roses, delicately petalled and aggressively thorned: sweetbriar, the apple-scented rose; dog rose, with its shell-pink flowers; the deep-pink downy rose; and the rich, cream-coloured field rose, which blooms last of all.

The warmth of the sun and the profusion of flowers bring out swarms of insects. Bees of all kinds buzz merrily, busily bustling from flower to flower, gold-dusted with pollen; butterflies sunbathe languidly after sipping their fill from overflowing nectaries, while hover flies, livery-bright, hang motionless over the umbellifers which decorate the hedgerows like lace.

The summer solstice – the longest day of the year, when the sun is at its highest – falls on 21–22 June. There are many stone circles in England, some as much as four thousand years old, positioned to mark the significant solstice dates; some of these circles are visited by people who wish to welcome the rising sun at the summer and winter solstices and the autumn and winter equinoxes.

In pagan times, throughout Europe, midsummer fires blazed on sacred high points which were believed to be focuses of the earth energy system. These ceremonial bonfires were lit on Midsummer Eve, a night that was believed to be particularly magical. The hazardous act of jumping over the bonfire was believed to bring the jumper fertility and good fortune.

In medieval times the Church tried to stop the midsummer rites, imposing in their place the celebration of the birthday of John the Baptist on 24 June; but the observance of Midsummer remained as pagan in spirit as May Day. The two festivals had much in common, including raising the maypole or 'summer pole', dancing and hilltop fires.

The electrical discharges
that flicker around ships
during storms are called
Saint Elmo's fire. This is
said to be a sign of his
protection.

1	
2	*Saint Elmo's Day, the patron saint of sailors*
3	
4	
5	
6	
7	

8   JUNE

9   *Saint Columba's Day*

Saint Columba's Day is the luckiest day in the year in the Scottish Highlands, especially when it falls on a Thursday.

10

11   *Saint Barnabas's Day. Saint Barnabas is invoked as a peacemaker*

On Saint Barnabas's Day it was customary to deck houses and churches with garlands of roses and sweet woodruff.

12

13   *Feast Day of Saint Antony of Padua*

Saint Antony is invoked for the finding of lost property.

14

BUTTERFLIES IN JUNE

Large white, small white, green-veined white, wood white, Duke of Burgundy fritillary, peacock, red admiral, painted lady, small tortoise-shell, white admiral, green hairstreak, large blue, brimstone, swallowtail, map butterfly, small heath, wall brown, apollo, purple emperor, Camberwell beauty, large tortoise-shell, comma, marbled white, grayling, meadow brown, ringlet, large heath.

WILDFLOWERS IN JUNE

Dog rose, yellow iris, honeysuckle, hedge woundwort, common elder, flax, lady's bedstraw, meadow cranesbill, foxglove, white, or Dutch, clover, common poppy, creeping thistle, corncockle, bindweed, self-heal, yellow rattle, cornflower.

'Bathed in buttercups to the dewlap, the roan cows standing in the golden lake watched the hours… On their broad brows the year falls gently; their great beautiful eyes, which need but a tear or a smile to make them human… in these eyes, as in a mirror, nature is reflected.'

from *Wild Flowers* by Richard Jefferies

'And if we sell you our land, you must keep it apart and sacred, as a place where even the white man can go to taste the wind that is sweetened by the meadow's flowers.'

Chief Seattle

NATURE IN JUNE

The tadpoles of frog, toad and newt are growing fast. And so they must, for they have a precarious existence among hungry predators, and the tadpoles themselves prey on each other.

June is a month of munching caterpillars. Many birds depend on this source of food for successful breeding.

Caddis flies, with wings covered in fine brown hair, sit moth-like by the water's edge, rising in the evening to dance in swarms over the water surface.

Beaches, mudflats and gravel banks support many bivalve, or two-shell molluscs. The best known is the common cockle with its rounded shell and radiating ribs. Look along the tide line and you will surely find some interesting things cast up by the sea.

Deer breed in June. Fawns may be left in a secluded woodland area by their mother. Should you find one, don't handle it, and keep dogs well away, as the doe will return and will be put off by a strange scent.

Owl youngsters squeak loudly for food in the evening and early morning.

Keep a large shallow container of water in the garden. Birds will come down to bathe and night-time visitors, such as hedgehogs and red foxes, will come to drink.

Common blue butterflies feed on clover; at night they sleep in groups of three or four, clinging to a blade of grass.

Young shrews twitter in the grass, while the adults climb tall grasses to feed on insects.

Dragonflies and damselflies shine like jewels in the sun, darting in a shimmer of emerald and sapphire, enhancing the magic of a river.

At noon on 21 June in Chartres Cathedral, in France, a ray of white light falls on a mark set in the floor. The light shines through a specially positioned piece of plain glass set in the stained-glass window of Saint Apollinaire, in the south transept. This is a remnant of the ancient technique of determining orientation; the direction or shadow is closely related to solar and geographical phenomena.

15 *Saint Vitus's Day, the patron saint of dancers, actors and mummers*

16

17

18

19

20

21 *The summer solstice – the longest day of the year*

22 *The sun enters the House of Cancer*   **JUNE**

23 *Midsummer Eve or Johnsmas Eve*

Midsummer Eve is the witches' night, and bonfires are made on the hills in many places.

24 *Midsummer Day – the Feast of the Nativity of Saint John the Baptist*

Saint John's emblem is a lamb, and so he is the patron saint of shepherds; because he lived – while in the wilderness – on locusts and wild honey, he is also the protector of beekeepers.

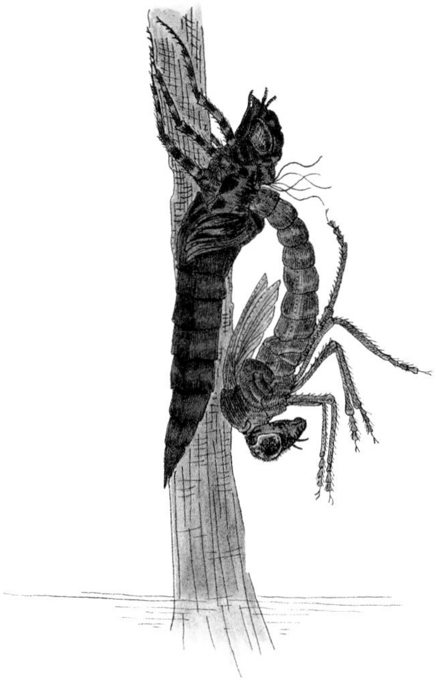

25

26

27

28

'White owls seem not (but in this I am not positive) to hoot at all: all that clamorous hooting appears to me to come from the wood kinds. The white owl does indeed snore and hiss in a tremendous manner; and these menaces well answer the intention of intimidating; for I have known a whole village to be up in arms on such an occasion, imagining the church-yard to be full of goblins and spectres.'

from *The Natural History of Selborne* by Gilbert White

'When all the birds are faint with the hot sun,
And hide in cooling trees, a voice will run
From hedge to hedge about the new-mown mead:
That is the grasshopper's – he takes the lead
In summer luxury, – he has never done
With his delights, for when tired out with fun,
He rests at ease beneath some pleasant weed.'

from *The Grasshopper and the Cricket* by
John Keats (1795–1821)

'The bird knows not the way it flies;
No one calls and feeds it;
It flies as the wings carry,
It feeds on what it finds.
That is the right way for you too...

The bird perches on a branch,
Starts at something that it sees,
Of a sudden flies, remembering something.
That is the bird's daily wont.
Do you think you are above it?'

The Way of the Bird by D. V. Gundappa,
(1889–1965), translated from Kannada

The male three-spined stickleback is
normally silver, but has a brilliant
breeding coloration. He builds a nest in
a sandy depression in shallow water,
using bits of plant glued together with a
kidney secretion, which is released
when the fish presses himself against
the vegetation he has gathered. When
the nest is finished, the red-bellied
male chooses a female and begins a
chain of interactions – very like a dance
sequence – which is carried out close to
the nest. The zigzag courtship dance
begins when the female becomes interested in the nest; the male then flirts
with her, twisting and turning in the
water. First the male leads – the female
follows him – the male shows her the
nest and induces her to enter it, by
pointing with his snout. When she
enters the nest, the male prods her
protruding tail, which induces her to
spawn. The whole sequence of actions
in this 'dance' is built up from sign
stimuli; at each stage in the chain, the
response of one partner is necessary for
the other to progress to the next stage
in the sequence.

JULY

July, the month of haymaking, is named in honour of Julius Caesar, whose Julian calendar was used in Europe for nearly sixteen centuries.

Until a few decades ago every farm that kept animals had to have hay for fodder; haytime is still an anxious and busy period in the agricultural year. Before the advent of modern machinery, the greater part of haymaking had to be done by hand; men, women and children did the work of strewing, turning, gathering, carting and ricking. These processes took a long time and exposed the hay to the perils of rainfall for a longer time. No wonder then, that humans devised methods (however unscientific) for predicting the weather at this time, choosing certain saints' days as key indicators of the weather to come. It is said that should it rain on Saint Mary's Day, 2 July, it will rain for a month. Saint Swithin's Day, 15 July, is the most crucial day of the year in weather lore; for if it rains on Saint Swithin's Day it will rain for forty days. To this day some farmers breathe a sigh of relief if these days are sunny.

Many people visit the seaside during the summer season, seeking the salt breezes and enjoying the mood changes of the sea itself. The unpredictable colour and movement of a seascape, varying with the weather conditions, are fascinating to behold; the clear horizon may suddenly be blurred by a squall, and a gentle, blue, rippling sea can quickly change to leaden grey with high, white-capped waves. The seashore is a complex habitat where the constantly changing tide affects the plants and animals living there. The incoming tide carries seaweeds and many small animals high up the shore, and the outgoing tide leaves some behind for us to wonder at.

Away from the sea, the countryside takes on a sultry look of dark reds, mauves and purples. There is heather on the hillsides, where emperor moth caterpillars feed, and on warm days, you may see lizards basking in the sun. Codlins and cream, purple loosestrife and policeman's helmets line the banks of streams and rivers, their long stems sheltering secretive water voles and providing resting places for sparkling winged dragonflies. Rosebay willowherb graces waste land everywhere; ragged robin grows in damp places, while red campion and black horehound bloom in woods and on hedgebanks. Vetches scramble along the hedgerow, and bittersweet, exotic and tempting, hangs its flowers among the hawthorn twigs. Foxgloves stand in battalions in woodland glades and in shady places, where their inviting purple bells offer pollen to any bold bee who will follow the crimson spotted way deep into the heart of the flower.

There is a key to this picture at the end of the book.

In the United States, Independence Day is familiarly known as the Fourth of July. The day commemorates the signing of the Declaration of Independence on 4 July 1776, when the Liberty Bell rang out for the independence of the new nation. The custom of building large bonfires, shooting off firecrackers and making a joyous noise generally on the Fourth, began during the revolutionary war. Today the holiday is marked by picnics, parades and firework displays.

1

2   *Saint Mary's Day*

3

4   *Old Midsummer Eve*
      American Independence Day

5   *Old Midsummer Day*

6

7

8

9

10

11

12

13

14   *Bastille Day*

Bastille Day is a national holiday in France. The Bastille was the name given to the castle of Saint-Antoine, which was used for centuries as a state prison. The building was a hated symbol of absolutism because it was used by the Crown as a place of arbitrary and secret imprisonment. On 14 July 1789, a Parisian mob stormed the Bastille, hoping to seize its store of ammunition; in it they found only seven prisoners. This event has come to symbolize the complex political upheaval known as the French Revolution.

BUTTERFLIES IN JULY

Large white, small white, green-veined white, wood white, apollo, brimstone, purple emperor, white admiral, Camberwell beauty, large tortoiseshell, peacock, red admiral, painted lady, heath fritillary, marbled white, grayling, meadow brown, ringlet, large heath, small heath, speckled wood, holly blue, swallowtail, gatekeeper, chalkhill blue.

WILDFLOWERS IN JULY

Common mallow, bell heather, ling (heather), field scabious, yarrow, imperforate Saint John's wort, meadowsweet, bramble, rosebay willowherb, kidney vetch, purple loosestrife, common toadflax, yellow water lily, bittersweet, yellow chamomile, harebell.

Fragrant meadowsweet, queen of the meadow, comes into bloom this month. In medieval times the leaves and flowers were used as a strewing herb, to freshen the floor of a house, for it was said that the smell 'made the heart merry'.

NATURE IN JULY

Male yellowhammers sing on hedge tops, while their mates sit on second clutches of eggs.

Young red foxes are being taught to hunt by their mother.

Bullfinch nesting is in full swing, and goldfinches are beginning to build their nests – their breeding is timed to coincide with seed crops rather than insects.

Honeysuckle, tobacco plants, night-scented stocks and evening primroses will attract the many night-flying moths.

Puss moth eggs and larvae can be found on the upper sides of the leaves of poplar and willow. The eggs are like tiny brown buns; the larvae are black when newly hatched, and easily recognized by the two slender black 'tails' which they waggle about when disturbed.

The marbled white butterfly lays her eggs this month, dropping them as she flies low over the grass. There is a good chance that they will fall on one of the grasses the caterpillar will eat, such as cocksfoot or sheep's fescue.

Earthworms lie out on damp nights, with their tails firmly anchored in their holes so that they are able to retreat quickly if disturbed.

During July and August birds become especially secretive as they moult. Adult birds must regenerate all their feathers over a short period. Worn plumage must be replaced or the birds will not be well insulated against the cold of winter.

Water shrew families swim like miniature black otters, in clear, deep water.

Dragonflies fly in tandem. The male goes in front, holding the female by the neck, with the clasper at the end of his abdomen. The female curves the tip of her abdomen around to the male's reproductive organs and collects his sperm. The eggs are laid shortly afterwards.

Rain on Saint Swithin's Day, according to tradition, 'blesses and christens the apples'. Apples should not be picked and eaten before this feast.

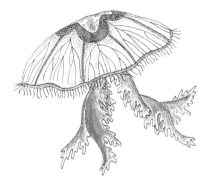

Common jellyfish

Legend tells us that Wilgefortis, daughter of the king of Portugal, took a vow of virginity. When her father tried to make her marry, she prayed for deliverance and at once sprouted a beard. Her suitors fled in horror, and her angry father had her crucified.

15 *Saint Swithin's Day*

16

17

18

19

20 *The Feast of Saint Wilgefortis, the original bearded lady*

21

22 *The Feast of Saint Mary Magdalene*

23

24 *The sun enters the House of Leo*

25 *The feast day of two saints for travellers, Saint Christopher and Saint James the Greater*

26 *The Feast of Saint Anne, mother of the Virgin Mary and patron saint of housewives*

27

28

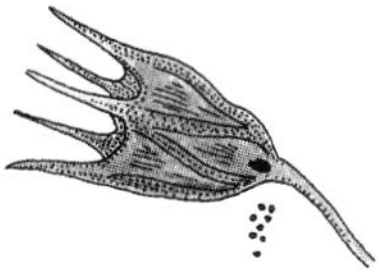

Saint Mary Magdalene is the patron saint of penitents and of reformed prostitutes.

Saint Christopher was a legendary giant who carried the Christ Child across a rushing river; he is therefore the patron saint of wayfarers. Saint James, one of the twelve Apostles, had his principal shrine at Santiago de Compostela in Spain. This important shrine drew pilgrims from all over Europe, and so Saint James is the patron saint of pilgrims.

'I saw the long line of the vacant shore,
The sea-weed and the shells upon the sand,
And the brown rocks left bare on every hand,
As if the ebbing tide would flow no more.
Then heard I, more distinctly than before,
The ocean breathe and its great breast expand,
And hurrying came on the defenceless land
The insurgent waters with tumultuous roar.'

from *The Tides* by H.W. Longfellow

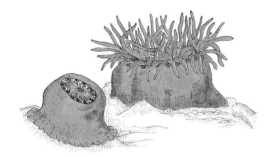

'I never liked the landsman's life,
The earth is aye the same;
Give me the ocean for my dower,
My vessel for my hame.
Give me the fields that no man ploughs,
The farm that pays no fee:
Give me the bonny fish that glance
So gladly through the sea.
When life's last sun goes feebly down,
And death comes to our door,
When all the world's a dream to us,
We'll go to sea no more.'

Scottish poem

'The fresh water attracts the fish, and these bring many terns, gulls and two kinds of cormorant. We saw also a pair of the beautiful black-necked swans, and several small sea-otters, the fur of which is held in such high estimation. In returning, we were again amused by the impetuous manner in which the heap of seals, old and young, tumbled into the water as the boat passed. They did not remain long under water, but rising, followed us with outstretched necks, expressing great wonder and curiosity.'

from *The Voyage of the Beagle* by Charles Darwin
(1809-82)

29	JULY
30	
31	

Various species of colourful anemones

AUGUST

August, the month of harvest, is named in honour of the first Roman emperor, Augustus, who held this to be his lucky month.

Augustus was born Caius Octavius, great nephew of Julius Caesar, who made the boy his heir without his knowledge. The name Augustus was a title of honour granted by the Senate in 27 B.C.

In August the leaves often begin to look tired and dusty and early fruits begin to ripen in the hedgerows; few birds are to be seen; golden tints appear in the sea of bracken fronds; and the parachute seeds of rosebay willowherb fill the air. In the fields the merry chirp of grasshoppers can be heard, as they play their strange, stridulant love songs to would-be mates.

Behind the shore, close to the sea, where waves splash salty spray onto the pebble- and boulder-strewn strand, you will find some fascinating and colourful plants. Tufts of sea pinks, anchored firmly by long roots which go deep into rock crevices; white sea campion with sepal tubes inflated into pinkish bladders beneath each flower; lilac-coloured sea lavender, which retains its form and colour for many months after the end of summer. Look for prickly sea holly with its tough, spiky, holly-like leaves, which protect the plant from caterpillars; the closely packed flower heads are so blue that the colour spreads into the leaves. The small pink flowers of sea milkwort spread like a thick carpet over the sand and shingle; its blue-green, oval leaves store water, and the whole compact mass of the plant reduces evaporation. Mauve sea asters grow at the mercy of the winds and tides; while on cliffs and rocks yellow-green samphire blooms. This plant was once used as a pickled condiment; Samuel Pepys records being given a barrel of samphire on 21 September 1660, and Shakespeare writes, in *King Lear:* '...half way down, hangs one who gathers samphire, dreadful trade.'

Harvest time is the culmination of the labours of the agricultural year. In the past there were many local harvest customs and rituals, which died out only when machinery took over the harvesting.

Harvest was a time for rejoicing, but correct procedures had to be followed in order to guarantee the success of the next harvest. The cutting of the last sheaf was a critical point, and the form of this ceremony varied from area to area. The last remaining stand of corn was called the 'neck' – a Norse word meaning 'sheaf'. The neck held

the spirit of the corn, and no one wanted to make the final cut and
'kill' it. So the reapers would stand at a distance and throw their
sickles at the corn, in turn, until it was finally cut; the responsibility
for the 'kill' was then a joint one. These last corn stalks were often
twisted into a corn 'dolly', which was believed to contain the spirit of
the corn and which was kept in the farmhouse until the spring
ploughing, when it was returned to the soil.

'It is the harvest moon! On guilded vanes
And roofs of villages, on woodland crests
And their aerial neighbourhood of nests
Deserted, on the curtained window-panes
Of rooms where children sleep, on country lanes
And harvest fields, its mystic splendour rests!
Gone are the birds that were our summer guests,
With the last sheaves return the labouring wains!
All things are symbols: the external shows
Of nature have their image in the mind,
As flowers and fruits and falling of the leaves;
The song birds leave us at the summer's close,
Only the empty nests are left behind,
And piping of the quail among the sheaves.'

from *The Harvest Moon* by H.W. Longfellow

Lammas Day, or 'loaf-mass', is the festival for the beginning of harvest. On this day the first cut sheaf of corn, or the bread made from it, was blessed and offered in church.

1	*Lammas Day*
2	
3	
4	*Saint Dominic's Day, founder of the Dominican order*
5	
6	
7	

9

10 *Saint Lawrence's Day*

Saint Lawrence is the patron saint of bakers, confectioners and cooks.

11

12 *Old Lammas Day*

13 *The Feast of Saint Cassian*

Saint Cassian is the patron saint of schoolteachers. Cassian himself was a very severe teacher who was stabbed to death with iron pen nibs by his pupils.

14

BUTTERFLIES IN AUGUST

Large white, green-veined white,
wood white, brimstone, purple
emperor, peacock, red admiral,
painted lady, small tortoiseshell,
comma, map butterfly, heath
fritillary, marbled white, grayling,
meadow brown, gatekeeper, ringlet,
speckled wood, wall brown, small
heath, holly blue, large blue,
chalkhill blue, common blue, small
copper.

WILDFLOWERS IN AUGUST

Greater willowherb, greater
knapweed, devil's bit scabious,
marjoram.

'Sky, earth, sea were once without expression
Lacking the festive magic
Of the seasons. Your branches gave
Music its first refuge, invented the songs
In which the restless wind, clothing
With an all-enveloping melody
Her invisible body, edging
Her shawl with prismatic tune – first knew
Herself. You were the first to trace
A living image of beauty on the earth's clay canvas
By absorbing the living power of the sun …
Silent tree, by restraining valour
With patience, you revealed creative
Power in its peaceful form. And we come
To your shade to learn the art of peace,
And to hear the word of silence …'

from *In Praise of Trees* by Rabindranath Tagore,
(1861–1941), translated from Bengali

NATURE IN AUGUST

At the seaside, sea lavender makes the salt marsh purple while bright pink sea bindweed winds through the vegetation on sandy beaches.

August is a splendid month for watching grasshoppers, birds and insects noisily court their mates in the meadows. Hover flies display their best stunt flying in the still air of a summer's day. Parties of insectivorous birds comb the woods, concentrating on feeding. There may be blue tits, great tits, coal tits, marsh tits, long-tailed tits accompanied by goldcrests, and perhaps a treecreeper or nuthatch.

On a still evening, sit quietly, with a good view of a clear patch of sky, and wait. As night falls, bats will emerge to weave and dive as they snap up hundreds of insects.

Owl youngsters are being driven away from the nest to fend for themselves, after being dependent on their parents for several months.

Red fox cubs are dispersing, perhaps travelling long distances before they find an unoccupied territory.

You may find an adder sunning itself on a country path. They slide away quickly when they feel the vibrations of a footfall, so approach quietly if you want to have a good look.

Young house martins and swallows gather on wires and roofs of houses. These are the young of early broods who have learned how to feed efficiently and to recognize local landmarks. Now is the time to put up new swift and martin nest boxes, as the young birds will see and remember suitable nest sites before they fly away to winter in Africa.

The first flush of autumn fungi will appear towards the end of the month, if conditions are damp enough. Field and parasol mushrooms form colonies in pastures and along woodland edges. Pine woods shelter the scarlet-capped *Russula emetica* and the blood red *Russula sanguinea,* whereas the orange-red *Russula lepida* flourishes in deciduous woodland.

The death and entrance into Heaven of the Virgin Mary.

Saint Roch was a selfless fourteenth-century plague doctor; his name is invoked against all infectious diseases.

Saint Helena was the formidable mother of the Emperor Constantine. Her name is invoked against fire, lightning and tempest.

15	*The Feast of the Assumption*
16	*Saint Roch's Day*
17	
18	*Saint Helena's Day*
19	
20	
21	

22

23 *The sun enters the House of Virgo*

24 *Bartlemas, the Feast of Saint Bartholomew*

According to legend, Saint Bartholomew was martyred by being skinned alive. Perhaps for this reason, he is the patron saint of tanners, skinners, butchers, bookbinders and leatherworkers.

25

26

27

28

'… we saw nothing in particular, excepting on one day a great shoal of porpoises, many hundreds in number. The whole sea was in places furrowed by them; and a most extraordinary spectacle was presented, as hundreds, proceeding together by jumps, in which their whole bodies were exposed, thus cut the water.'

from *The Voyage of the Beagle* by Charles Darwin

Hermit crab

'The water was more to me than water, and the sun than sun. The gleaming rays on the water in my palm held me for a moment, the touch of the water gave me something from itself. A moment and the gleam was gone, the water flowing away, but I had had them. Beside the physical water and the physical light I had received from them their beauty; they had communicated to me this silent mystery.'

from *Meadow Thoughts* by Richard Jefferies

29	AUGUST

30	

31	

'The sea awoke at midnight from its sleep,
And round the pebbly beaches far and wide
I heard the first wave of the rising tide
Rush onward with uninterrupted sweep;
A voice out of the silence of the deep,
A sound mysteriously multiplied
As of a cataract from the mountain's side,
Or roar of winds upon a wooded steep.'

from *The Sound of the Sea*
by H.W. Longfellow

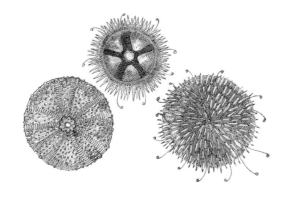

Sea urchins and a comb jelly
(top of page)

SEPTEMBER

September is the seventh month of the Roman calendar. It is a month with a distinctive quality of its own; during the first two weeks or so, summer is still with us, but then unmistakable signs of autumn begin to show themselves. Hazel leaves become splashed with yellow, spiders' webs glisten in the early morning mists, and fruits ripen in the hedgerows and orchards.

This is a time of glowing colours: of luscious blackberries, dark, gleaming sloes, shiny scarlet rosehips, deep red hawthorn berries, russet apples and brown nuts. Fungi of all shapes and hues speckle the fields, cluster around tree roots and sprout from trunks and branches. There are red and white fly agaric toadstools and tawny grisettes flourishing in birch woods while in beech and oak woods there may be black and white magpie ink-caps, the orange-red devil's boletus

and Russulas of orange, red, magenta, purple and green. On heaths and amongst grasses, look for scarlet hoods, pink meadow-caps, brown-scaled parasol mushrooms and violet-stemmed blewits.

Apples have been grown and eaten for thousands of years. Ovid, a Latin poet who lived from 43 B.C. to A.D. 17, wrote: 'It is more pleasing to pluck an apple from the branch which you have seized, than to take one up from a graven dish.'

It is not known when apples were first used in pies or puddings, but the use of apples in a fermented form, or as a distilled spirit, must be as old as the invention of wine.

Heaven, according to Teutonic mythology, is a vale of apple trees tended by the goddess Idun. The apples gave the gods perpetual youth and immortality. A Christian legend about the Virgin Mary may have its roots in this mythology. According to this legend, one day, while Mary, heavy with child, was out walking she came to an apple tree laden with fruit; she could not reach the branches to pick an apple, so the tree lowered its branches for her. This is why, we are told, many apple trees still have branches that hang down.

By September the young frogs born earlier in the year are hunting for food on land. Here most are taken by predators, leaving only a few to survive to adulthood. Overwintering tadpoles are not uncommon in the north of Europe, scarcity of food or cold conditions having inhibited their development.

'The shining water that moves in the streams and rivers is not just water but the blood of our ancestors. If we sell you the land, you must remember that it is sacred, and you must teach your children that each ghostly reflection in the clear water of the lakes tells of events and memories in the life of my people.'

Chief Seattle

1	
2	
3	
4	*Old Saint Bartholomew's Day*
5	
6	
7	

8   *The Feast of the Nativity of the Virgin Mary*   **SEPTEMBER**

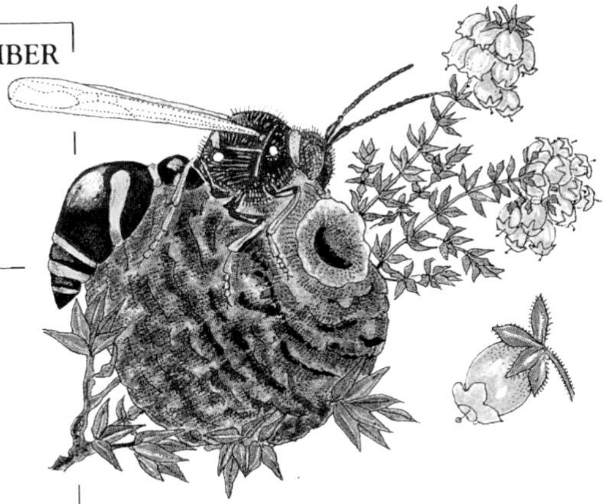

9

10

11

12

13

14   *Holy Cross or Holy Rood Day. Also called the Devil's Nutting Day*

September 14 is called the Devil's Nutting Day because it is said that hazelnuts collected on this day have magical properties. Look for two nuts on one stalk; these ward off toothache, rheumatism and witches' spells. But be careful, for if you pick the nuts before they are ripe bad luck will befall you.

BUTTERFLIES IN SEPTEMBER

Apollo, green-veined, white, brimstone, peacock, red admiral, painted lady, small tortoiseshell, comma, map butterfly, grayling, meadow brown, small heath, speckled wood, wall brown, small copper, chalkhill blue, common blue.

WILDFLOWERS IN SEPTEMBER

Many wildflowers are still in bloom in September, but they are beginning to set seed and prepare for winter. However, the woods and hedgerows are bright with ripening fruits; look for rosehips, hawthorn berries, horse-chestnuts, hazel nuts, elderberries, blackberries, sloes, crab apples and fruits of the guelder rose and wayfaring tree.

'The first day of September was almost the last of the real summer weather. It was very warm and the sky, at its zenith, was a deep ultramarine blue against which floated great, puffed-up, whipped-cream dollops of cloud with dazzling white crests and smoky, purplish-grey shadows … Everything had a tired, rather tattered, end-of-summer look, with brown seed-heads in place of flowers, leaves disfigured by caterpillars, patches of grass scorched brown by the heat and thistledown every-where, floating through the air in clusters and adhering to the bushes. Yet there was still a lot of colour, particularly in the thicket glades where fleabane mingled with water mint and ragwort. Butterflies were out in force, with peacocks, small tortoiseshells, small whites and meadow browns all in good numbers.'

from *A Secret Landscape* by Benjamin Perkins (1932–). Reproduced by courtesy of the author

Blackberries continue to flower and fruit until the first frosts.

NATURE IN SEPTEMBER

Fluttering parties of goldfinches sway on downy thistle heads, ringing out their clear, bell-like calls. No wonder that the collective term for them is 'a chime'.

Badgers discard old bedding material and drag fresh grass, straw and bracken into their setts.

Look for the large, black- and orange-banded rove beetle. These beetles feed in the gill structures of mushrooms.

Be sure to have a pile of logs or stones by your pond; this year's frogs, toads and newts will need somewhere safe and damp to hide.

Grey seal cows congregate on rocky coasts, to produce their single pups, between now and November. The pups are fed with their mother's rich, fat-laden milk for up to three weeks; then they are deserted and have to fend for themselves.

The red deer's rutting season begins in September, when stags fight for mates and for status within the herd.

As the blackberries become more juicy, they attract butterflies such as comma, speckled wood and red admiral, who suck up the juices with long hollow tongues.

Spiders' webs glisten in the early morning mists of September, linking grass blade to grass blade with silver threads. The garden spider builds a classic orb web, but the little money spiders spin hammock-like webs which are often carried over long distances on air streams. Money spiders themselves seem to take to the air at will; by releasing silk from their spinnerets they can become airborne at a moment's notice.

After a very dry summer, beech, elm, oak and poplar trees shed limbs in a self-pruning exercise. This self-amputation is to reduce water uptake, and prior to the operation the tree has cut off supplies to the limb in question.

Autumn colours begin to creep into leaves, and before the month has ended lime, poplar and birch leaves will be yellow-gold.

On stubble fields you may see a solitary pheasant cock, strutting along with his hens in close attendance.

Swallows gather in flocks, preparing to migrate for the winter. Their departure usually coincides with Michaelmas Day, 29 September, which also traditionally marks the end of harvesting.

Saint Ninian's plant symbol is the herb southernwood. This plant also bears the name 'lad's love' and was given by bachelors to the girl of their choice.

15	
16	*Saint Ninian's Day*
17	
18	
19	
20	
21	*Autumn Equinox* *Saint Matthew's Day*

22   SEPTEMBER

23

24 *The sun enters the House of Libra*

25

26

27 *The Feast of saints Cosmas and Damian, the patron saints of doctors,*
        apothecaries and barbers

28 *Michaelmas Eve*

The Jewish New Year, Rosh
Hashanah, falls in
September. This ten-day
period of penitence
(sometimes lasting into
October) is followed by
Yom Kippur, the Day of
Atonement, a solemn day
of fasting.

'September 12th 1774. Wasps nesting far from neighbourhoods feed on flowers, and catch flies and caterpillars to carry to their young. Wasps make their nests with the raspings of sound timber; hornets with what they gnaw from decayed. These particulars of wood are neaded [sic] up with a mixture of saliva from their bodies, and moulded into combs.'

Gilbert White

A heavy crop of hips, haws and rowan berries portends a hard winter.

'The exceeding beauty of the earth, in her splendour of life, yields a new thought with every petal. The hours when the mind is absorbed by beauty are the only hours when we really live, so that the longer we can stay among these things so much the more is snatched from inevitable Time.'

from The Pageant of Summer by Richard Jefferies

'Time is a sort of river of passing events, and strong is its current; no sooner is a thing brought to sight than it is swept by and another takes its place, and this too will be swept away …'

from The Meditations of Marcus Aurelius
(121–180)

29	*Michaelmas, the feast of Saint Michael*	SEPTEMBER
30		

Saint Michael is the patron saint of knights and warriors. He was captain of the Host of Heaven and cast Satan and his wicked angels out of Paradise.

Michaelmas is traditionally the last day for picking blackberries, for it is said that when Saint Michael threw the Devil out of Paradise he landed in a blackberry bush; the Devil was so badly scratched that he spat on the bush and rendered the fruits inedible.

'Every part of this earth is sacred to my people. Every shining pine needle, every sandy shore, every mist in the dark woods, every clearing and humming insect is holy in the memory and experience of my people.'

Chief Seattle

'Great men die and are forgotten,
Wise men speak; their words of wisdom
Perish in the ears that hear them,
Do not reach the generations
That, as yet unborn, are waiting
In the great mysterious darkness
Of the speechless days that shall be.'

from *The Song of Hiawatha*
by H. W. Longfellow (1807–82)

OCTOBER

October is the eighth month of the Roman calendar and the month of leaf fall.

There is gold in the mellow autumn atmosphere; gold in the leaves fluttering and trembling in the wind and gold in the fallen apples lying in the withering straw-coloured grass. Queen wasps gorge themselves on the decaying fruit in the orchard and refresh themselves with nectar from the yellow-green ivy flowers, starry amid the dark, glossy leaves. Queen wasps and queen bumble bees must feed well before going into hibernation, for they carry the sperm that will fertilize the eggs they will lay in the spring, in order to continue the species.

There are fewer and fewer insects to be seen as the weather grows cooler; late butterflies, bluebottles and greenbottles feed on the last of the blackberries before finding a sheltered niche in which to overwinter. The swarms of insects that filled the summer air have disappeared, as have the birds who fed on them; these migrant birds left for sunnier climes with the increasingly short days and colder weather. Other birds arrive from colder countries farther north to take advantage of the autumn fruits, while some of our resident birds begin to sing again, after their quiet period at the end of the breeding season.

Voles make the most of the abundant food; water voles store beechmast in their riverside holes, while bank voles climb up into the hedges, collecting hips and haws. Field voles are very vulnerable when their runways are not sheltered by long grasses, so they try to stay well hidden; but there are many sharp eyes waiting to spot them, and they become victims of kestrels and owls, who quarter the open ground.

As temperatures fall, so do the leaves. In Europe there is a saying that 'October with green leaves means a severe winter'. The country weather sages traditionally resort to predictions about the winter weather at this time of the year. Some believe they can tell what the weather will be like by observing how deep snails bury themselves, how deep mice dig their tunnels or how high ants build their nest mounds. Others predict the weather by the numbers of fruits and berries; many berries forecast a bad winter – never mind that they were formed in a good spring.

Samhain, the last evening of October, was the beginning of the Celtic year, when the cold and darkness of winter began. Festivals with bonfires were held at this time to celebrate 'Winter's Eve' and the beginning of a new year. In an attempt to Christianize this pagan festival, the Church adopted 1 November as the feast of All Saints or All Hallows. So the festival of Samhaim became All Hallows Even or Hallowe'en, when witches and supernatural beings are still remembered and impersonated by children and adults alike.

The black cat, traditional companion of witches, is often associated with Hallowe'en.

'Nearer human were their powers,
Closer knit their life with ours.
Hands had stroked them, which are cold,
Now for years, in churchyard mould;
Comrades of our past were they,
Of that unreturning day.'

from *Poor Matthias* by Matthew Arnold
(1822–88)

The harvest-end celebration was traditionally a gargantuan meal, provided by the farmer for all his employees. It is now the custom for churches of all denominations to hold a service of thanksgiving in late September or early October; flowers, sheaves of corn, fruits and vegetables are used as decorations, and are then given to the poor and elderly of the parish.

Saint Francis of Assisi was the founder of the Franciscan order of friars. He is remembered for his humility and love of all creation.

1

2

3

4   *Saint Francis's Day*

5

6

7

8	**OCTOBER**

9 *Saint Denis's Day, patron saint of Franc_*

10 *Old Michaelmas Day*

Old Michaelmas Day often brings a spell of fine weather called 'Michaelmas Spring'.

11

12

13 *Saint Edward the Confessor's Day, founder of Westminster Abbey*

14

BUTTERFLIES IN OCTOBER

Peacock, red admiral, painted lady, small tortoiseshell, brimstone.

WILDFLOWERS IN OCTOBER

Ivy is the last flower to bloom in the year. Its yellow, starry blooms are full of nectar; these are the last feeding stations for flies, hover flies and wasps. The flowers are formed only on mature plants, and the leaves on these flowering shoots are bright green, diamond- shaped, contrasting with the familiar lobed leaves.

'What is man without the beasts? If all the beasts were gone, man would die from great loneliness of spirit, for whatever happens to the beast also happens to man. All things are connected. Whatever befalls the earth befalls the sons of the earth.'

Chief Seattle

'October 5th 1783. In the High-wood, under the thick trees, and among the dead leaves, where there was no grass, we found a large circle of *Fungi* of the *Agaric* kind, which included many beeches within its ring. Such circles are often seen on turf, but not usually in covert.'

Gilbert White

'All things brown and yellow and red are brought out by the autumn sun; the brown furrows freshly turned where the stubble was yesterday, the brown bark of trees, the brown fallen leaves, the brown stalks of plants; the red haws, the red unripe blackberries, red bryony berries, reddish-yellow fungi, yellow hawkweed, yellow ragwort, yellow hazel-leaves; not a speck of yellow, red or brown the yellow sunlight does not find out.'

from *Under the Acorns* by Richard Jefferies

NATURE IN OCTOBER

The reds and golds of the autumn leaves and the glowing hues of fruits and berries bring a welcome brightness to the shortening days.

There are many mushrooms and toadstools of all colours and shapes to be seen in October. The pretty but poisonous fly agaric lives in association with birch trees. *Geastrum quadrifidum,* the earthstar, grows in pine litter, where its round, greyish spore body is carried aloft on a star-like pedestal. Bird's nest fungi, when mature, are cup-like and carry egg-shaped, spore-bearing bodies. Look for these fungi on conifer and frondose twigs.

Earwigs retreat into a soil cavity to overwinter. The female lays about forty eggs at this time, covering them with her body to keep them safe until they hatch in spring.

Ladybirds cluster together to spend the winter roosting under logs or in the crevices of walls, or they come indoors to nestle in dark corners around a window.

Birds and mammals enjoy eating berries and soft fruits, but they look for the hard fruits too. Beechmast is energy-rich; nuts of all kinds are durable, so they can be stored as a late winter food supply. Jays and squirrels carry acorns away from the parent oak, burying them in the ground. Some acorns are not eaten, and their germination plays an important part in the spread of oak woods. Mice store acorns, hazelnuts, sweet chestnuts and berries in the old nests of blackbirds and thrushes.

The nuthatch is very busy. He flies to a tree or post, and, jamming a nut into a crevice, he chips at the hard coat, shell flying around him, to reach the soft kernel.

Plan your winter bird-feeding area now. A bird table may be erected on a post or hung from a branch or bracket, where there is no easy access for cats. It is not essential to put a roof over the table, but it would keep the worst of the rain off.

Different birds enjoy different foods, so put a good mixture out each day: fruit, nuts, mixed seed, coarse raw oats and kitchen scraps. Do **not** give birds salted nuts or desiccated coconut.

The Feast of Tabernacles, or Sukkoth, is the Jewish harvest festival. Booths made from branches and adorned with fruit and vegetables are built and used for meals during the ten-day-long observances.

15

16

17

18 *Saint Luke's Day*

19

20

21

22 OCTOBER

23

24 *The sun enters the House of Scorpio*

25 *Saint Crispin and Saint Crispinian's Day, the patron saints of shoemakers*

Crispin and his brother Crispinian were martyred in 287 in Soissons, France, for preaching Christianity. They were greatly venerated during the Middle Ages, and their day acquired additional fame as the date of the Battle of Agincourt (1415), celebrated by Shakespeare in *Henry V*.

26

27

28 *Saint Simon and Saint Jude's Day*

Saint Simon is the patron saint of woodcutters and Saint Jude is the patron of lost causes and is invoked by those who are desperate.

A spell of fine weather during the latter half of the month is called 'St Luke's little summer' in Britain.

In eastern and central United States, too, there is often a spell of warm, dry weather in late October or November; this is known as Indian summer – possibly because Indians used to gather in their winter stores during this time.

Hallowe'en is the night of the dead, when ghosts visit the earth and witches and evil spirits are at their most powerful. On no account must you allow your fire to go out tonight, or the evil ones will enter the house.

One of the games traditionally played at Hallowe'en is bobbing for apples. Apples are floated in a tub of water, and, with hands tied behind the back, the player must catch and hold an apple between the teeth. In earlier times, a fortunate girl who won an apple would sleep with it under her pillow, when she would surely dream of her lover. Another superstition was that if the girl stood before a mirror, eating the apple while brushing her hair, then her future husband would look over her shoulder into the glass. But if she turned around, he would vanish.

The Romans had a festival around the end of October, in honour of Pomona, goddess of fruit trees and special patroness of the apple orchard. At this festival, nuts and apples, tokens of the winter store of fruits, were roasted before great bonfires.

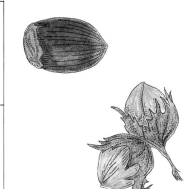

| |
| |
| 30 |

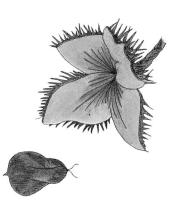

| 31 | *Hallowe'en, the eve of All Hallows, or All Saints' Day. The eve of Samhain or Winter's Eve, the last night of the Celtic year* |

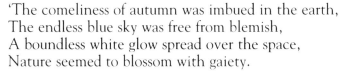

'The comeliness of autumn was imbued in the earth,
The endless blue sky was free from blemish,
A boundless white glow spread over the space,
Nature seemed to blossom with gaiety.

By the river bank, in the woods and in the caves
Slowly flowed the clear springs of water,
Their incessant sound has an appeal so rare,
For they sang the glory of victorious autumn.'

from *The Great Dance* by Ayodhya Singh Upadhyaya,
(1865–1941), translated from Hindi

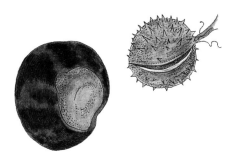

NOVEMBER

November is the ninth month of the Roman calendar and the beginning of the winter bleakness.

The days are short and the nights grow long and cold. Night is synonymous with darkness, and wherever good and bad are equated with light and darkness, night is regarded as symbolic of evil or death. Darkness is, as in Genesis, the original state; after the darkness came the light created by God. The analogy still holds in folklore; the night beings – hags, witches, devils, demons, trolls and goblins – are of the old belief, but in the light of day, God is all-powerful.

Very often, the eve of a particular feast day has been considered more important than the day itself; for example, Hallowe'en and Christmas Eve are more magical than All Hallows or Christmas Day. At cock crow, according to the old religion, the spirits of darkness lose their power, then the witches on their broomsticks, the dead out of their graves, the mischievous fairies and evil powers must all return to their resting places; for during the hours of daylight they dare not move to cause evil.

November is a dark month, when ghostly tales are told around the fire and shadows flit in the corners of the room. To quote Macbeth:

> 'Now o'er the one half world
> Nature seems dead, and wicked dreams abuse
> The curtain'd sleep …'

Nature does seem dead. By the end of the month the deciduous trees are bare of leaves; gardens and hedgerows are devoid of flowers; the landscape is dark and misty throughout the short days; and the world seems a dull and uninviting place. But wait; on a day of hoarfrost, with an orange-red sun hanging low in a pale sky, there are beautiful sights to see. The trees are etched in frosty white; the tall stems of umbellifers stand rigidly upright, the rays of their naked umbels spread wide and starry with rime; the flask-like heads of red and white campion stand firm on straw-coloured stalks and the narrow red-brown stems of dock are distinctively topped with the remains of dark, withered flowers.

Across the stillness there is the tip-tapping of a great spotted woodpecker, searching for larvae in a dead tree; an aggressive jay screams at a chattering squirrel foraging among the withered grass at the edge of a copse, while a kestrel hovers, keen eyes searching, soon to swoop on a luckless vole. By the stream, icicles drip from overhanging rocks and water plant stems are ringed by twinkling beads of ice which glitter in the sun.

As evening draws near, noisy rooks wend their way across the countryside to their roosts in woods or copses; wood pigeons roost in large numbers too, as do redwings and fieldfares who find an overgrown hedge or thicket a suitable roosting site. But of all the birds who roost collectively it is the starlings who draw the most attention; their flight lines converge and part as flock after flock joins the whole, to wheel and ebb, merge and spread until the sky is filled with a wonderful aerial display before night falls and the cold once more is master in the game of life.

Winter has a beauty of its own – cruel and remorseless perhaps; but to anyone interested in natural history it is a fascinating time. Birds and mammals are often easier to watch in winter when hunger makes them bolder. Even when the animal remains unseen, tracks may be obvious in mud or snow. Winter is a time for getting to know the flowerless plants – ferns, mosses and liverworts – and for appreciating the shapes of dried fruit capsules of flowering plants, discovering their mechanisms for seed dispersal.

In Catholic countries many people used to believe that the dead returned on All Souls' Day; in Italy, food was left for them on tables. Today in Italy, France and Germany families decorate the graves of their dead.

On the evening of All Saints' Day, 'soul-cakes' were given to the poor, who, in return, prayed for the souls of the dead. This tradition goes back to medieval times when 'soul-cakes' were baked on the death of a family member. The spiced cake represented the soul of the dead person – sins and all – and it was eaten by someone who didn't mind taking on the burden of another's sins. Poor people often begged for these cakes, offering to take the sins of the departed in exchange for the food. The Protestant Reformation abolished this practice, but the cakes continued to be eaten on All Souls' Day.

1	All Hallows, or the Feast of All Saints *Samhain, the Celtic New Year festival.*
2	*All Souls' Day, or Soulmass; a day for praying for the souls of the dead.*
3	
4	
5	*Guy Fawkes Night*
6	
7	

9

10   *Martinmas Eve, which is Old Hallowe'en*

11   *Martinmas; the festival of the beginning of winter*
       Teutonic New Year

12

13

14

Saint Martin, the patron saint of soldiers, died in 397. He was a Roman cavalry officer who shared his cloak with a beggar. The beggar later revealed himself to be Christ. Martinmas fires were lit in Germany throughout the Middle Ages; and later still the Dutch held fire festivals. In France, Martinmas is the time to burn old grape baskets in the square and drink and enjoy new wine.

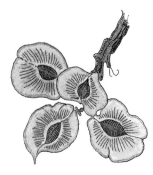

BUTTERFLIES IN NOVEMBER

In November butterflies begin to overwinter in a state of dormancy. This is a time of arrested development, or suspended animation; it may occur at any stage of the butterfly's life cycle: egg, caterpillar, pupa or adult. When winter arrives, bringing low temperatures and long nights, butterflies remain dormant, resting in one of the stages, according to the species, until spring.

WILDFLOWERS IN NOVEMBER

It is a challenge to find wildflowers in bloom at this gloomy time of the year, yet a careful search of the hedgerows is often rewarding. The evergreen shrub gorse has flowers throughout the year – hence the saying 'When the gorse is not in bloom, kissing is out of season'.

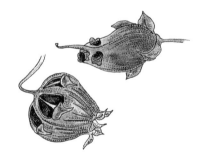

Martinmas was the traditional time for slaughtering all the cattle, sheep and pigs that could not be fed throughout the winter. The day of killing was followed by a feast of fresh meat.

In 1604 there was a plot to blow up the king and the members of the British Parliament. Guy Fawkes and his fellow conspirators were arrested in the cellars of the Palace of Westminster in time to prevent the explosion. On 5 November bonfires are made, an effigy of Guy Fawkes is burnt and there are fireworks to commemorate the 'Gunpowder Plot'.

NATURE IN NOVEMBER

Field voles become more and more vulnerable as the grass dies back and their runs become obvious to kestrels.

Starlings roost in large numbers in winter; at dusk there may be hundreds of thousands of individuals taking part in a fantastic aerial display.

Along field edges you might find the bright, yellow-orange, flattened-cup-shaped fungus *Scutellinia scutellata*. The underside of the fungus is covered with long dark hairs that curl over the coloured top – hence the common name of eyelash fungus.

Roe deer cast their antlers over the next few weeks. They will be the only deer growing new ones during the winter months.

Grass snakes hibernate among tree roots at the bottom of hedges, in dry stone walls or in compost heaps. They often twine together in groups during their hibernation.

Male mosquitoes are dead and the females are hibernating. Winter gnats dance harmlessly in swarms on sunny afternoons.

The mountain hare puts on its white winter coat, but retains the black tips to its ears. These hares are more sociable than brown hares and occasionally they form large groups.

Many birds have abandoned their solitary habit of summer days; instead they travel the countryside in flocks which grow in size, to find dwindling patches of food.

Wrens may gather in a hole in a thatch, or in a nest box, huddling together as a heat-saving device. Groups of six to ten long-tailed tits may cluster in a tight ball on a branch, to roost through a cold winter's night.

Older frogs burrow into a lair in the soft mud at the bottom of a pond to hibernate. Immature frogs, toads and newts hibernate away from water in any convenient hole in the ground, or in the warmth of a compost heap.

15

16

17

18

19

Saint Edmund was the Saxon king of East Anglia; he was martyred by the Vikings in 869.

20 *The Feast of Saint Edmund, the patron saint of sailors*

21

22 *Saint Cecilia's Day, patron saint of musicians*

23 *Saint Clement's Day – the patron saint of mariners and ironworkers, particularly blacksmiths*

24 *The sun enters the House of Sagittarius*

25 *Saint Catherine's Day, patron saint of all who use the wheel, especially carters, spinners and lacemakers*

26

27

28

According to legend, Saint Catherine was a Christian princess who refused to marry a pagan emperor. She was punished by being broken on a spiked wheel, hence 'catherine-wheel'.

Thanksgiving Day is celebrated in the United States on the fourth Thursday in November. It commemorates the first Thanksgiving feast held by the Plymouth colonists – or 'Pilgrim Fathers' – in 1621. The fifty-five settlers who had survived the first cruel winter gave thanks for their harvest of sweet corn, barley and peas and shared their feast, which included four wild turkeys, with friendly Indians.

'When the buffalo are all slaughtered, the wild horses all tamed, the secret corners of the forest heavy with scent of many men, and the view of ripe hills blotted by talking wires, where is the thicket? Gone. Where is the eagle? Gone. And what is it to say goodbye to the swift pony and the hunt? It is the end of living and the beginning of survival.'

Chief Seattle

'November 13th 1776. Nuthatches rap about on the trees. Crocus begin to sprout. The leaves of the medlar-tree are now turned of a bright yellow. One of the first trees that becomes naked is the walnut: the mulberry, and the ash, especially if it bears many keys, and the horse-chestnut comes next.'

Gilbert White

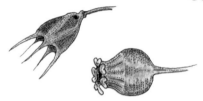

'He looked about for food, but found none. His short span of life was drawing to a close; even when at last he saw me, he could only run a few inches under cover of a dead clover plant. Though but a mouse, to me it was very wretched to see the chilled creature, so benumbed as to have almost lost its sense of danger.'

from *Outside London* by Richard Jefferies

The middle of November was the New Year of the ancient Germans. This was the time when the first frosts began to harden the ground and flocks were gathered in for the winter. The people celebrated with feasting; old worries and troubles were forgotten, and new duties and the promise of new bounties were welcomed. The Roman conquerors officially replaced this tradition with their own New Year, but the country people kept it going.

29	**NOVEMBER**
30	*Saint Andrew's Day – Saint Andrew is the patron saint of Scotland; of fishermen and fishmongers*

'Please to remember the fifth of November
Gunpowder, treason and plot.
I see no reason why gunpowder treason
Should ever be forgot.'

Old rhyme

'The south wind always brings wet weather,
The north wind wet and cold together.
The west wind always brings the rain,
And the east wind blows it back again.'

Traditional verse

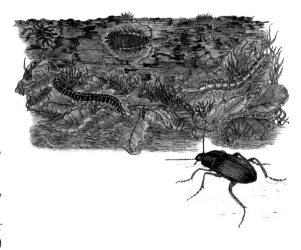

'An owl that in a barn
Sees a mouse creeping in the corn,
Sits still and shuts his round blue eyes,
As if he slept, until he spies
The little beast within his reach
Then starts, and seizes on the wretch.'

from *Hudibras* by Samuel Butler
(1612–80)

DECEMBER

December is the tenth month of the Roman calendar and is the darkest time of the year.

The days grow shorter still as we approach the winter solstice, and the need for some sort of artificial light – a need both physical and psychological – becomes more pressing. In the days when light was hard to come by, people found it important to hold festivals intended to banish the darkness. These festivals are found in many cultures, and include Diwali – the Hindu Festival of Lights, the Jewish Hanukkah and the Swedish Feast of Saint Lucia.

Saint Lucia, or Lucy, was a fourth-century martyr of Syracuse in Sicily. Her day, 13 December, is one of the darkest and shortest days in the year, and a time when people need extra nourishment and cheer. The name Lucy means 'light' and ancient documents tell of young girls, dressed in white with crowns of candles in their hair, serving their masters and mistresses. 'Lucia morning' is still celebrated in Sweden, where many communities, offices and schools choose a Lucia-girl to serve coffee, saffron rolls, ginger biscuits and sometimes glögg, a mulled wine. She is often accompanied by attendants also dressed in white; the girls have glitter in their hair, and the boys wear conical hats with stars on the top.

There is no historical record as to the exact date of the birth of Jesus Christ. At first, the time of the celebration of His birth varied from place to place; some churches observed it in December, some in January and others in April or May. It seems possible that 25 December was established as Christ's Mass, or Christmas, during the fourth century, to coincide with the beginning of the great pagan winter festival, when many people throughout Europe gathered together to make merry. The early Christian leaders tried to stop the dancing and drinking, but the general merriment of the ancient festival could not be eradicated.

By grafting new customs onto the old and making new symbols from ancient ones, Chuarch and people reached a compromise, and the new festival came into being. By the Middle Ages Christmas had become the greatest festival of the year. Churches were decorated, plays about the Nativity were enacted, carols were sung, and there was feasting and merrymaking.

During the fourteenth and fifteenth centuries, Christmas festivities were extremely elaborate, often lasting until Epiphany, or Twelfth Night; all work was forgotten and feasting and celebrations took over. A master of ceremonies, called the Lord of Misrule, was chosen – theoretically by chance; a cake was served, and he whose slice contained the lucky bean, coin or charm was elected. The Lord of Misrule led the revels and was obeyed by everyone during the celebrations.

During the sixteenth and seventeenth centuries, Puritans attempted to prohibit festivities at Christmas; they declared it to be a day of fasting and prayer. But Christmas could not be cancelled, and although it became more subdued, it survived as a bright, cheerful festival.

The observance of the Christmas festival spread all over the Christian world, but the date on which it is celebrated differs, and the customs vary greatly from one country to another.

Holly, ivy and mistletoe are linked with the midwinter rites of a pre-Christian era; all were considered to be magical plants because they bear leaves and fruits at an otherwise dead time of year. Holly berries were said to be powerful against witchcraft, but also to represent Christ's blood. Ivy, too, was a protection from witchcraft, but also symbolized immortality, while mistletoe, whose pagan associations were so strong that it is still not tolerated in church, continues to be hung in homes, where it witnesses fond kisses beneath its berried sprigs.

Hanukkah, the Jewish Festival of Lights, falls in early December. It commemorates the rededication of the Temple in Jerusalem in 164 B.C. after the overthrow of Syrian rule. On each night of the festival another candle is lit in the *menorah*, an eight-branched candlestick.

Saint Nicholas was a fourth-century bishop of Myra in Asia Minor. He is said to have saved three young girls from prostitution, by throwing each of them a golden ball through their window one night, to use as dowries. In this way he became the patron saint of children, and his nocturnal gifts are perpetuated in the gifts left by Santa Claus – Saint Nicholas. Pawnbrokers use his three golden balls as a sign of their trade.

1

2

3

4 *Saint Barbara's Day. Saint Barbara is the patron saint of artillery men*

5 *Saint Nicholas's Eve, when children in Germany and the Netherlands put out their boots or shoes for presents*

6 *The Feast of Saint Nicholas. Saint Nicholas is the patron saint of children and pawnbrokers*

7

8	DECEMBER
9	
10	
11	
12	*Saint Finnian's Night in the Scottish Highlands and Islands*
13	*Saint Lucy's Day* *In Sweden, Saint Lucia's Day, Little Yule or the Festival of Light*
14	

On Saint Finnian's night it is very unlucky to go to bed supperless; anyone who does so is likely to be carried away by the fairies.

VANISHING BUTTERFLIES

Many butterflies have declined in numbers, some because of subtle climatic changes and modern farming techniques. But the different species are associated with particular habitats, so species disappear when trees are felled, when marshes are drained and when old meadows are ploughed up.

FLOWERS IN DECEMBER

In these days of forced early bulbs and hothouse plants it is difficult to imagine a flowerless winter. The Christmas rose, or black hellebore, bravely opens its waxy petals for the winter solstice, to drive away demons and dispel melancholy.

Evergreens of all sorts are natural symbols of the continuation of plant life throughout the dark period of the year. Holly was such a magical tree that it was saved from the axe in days gone by, as it was considered unlucky to cut it down. Red is a magical colour which wards off evil, so the holly, with its red berries, when brought into the house, kept away goblins, demons and witches, from Christmas Eve to Candlemas Eve when the holly was put outside and left to die away. Mistletoe was the sacred plant of early man; it remains green when its host tree is apparently dead, and it is suspended between Earth and Heaven. Kissing under the mistletoe is probably linked with the ancient marriage rites; for mistletoe not only keeps the witches at bay but is also said to be an aphrodisiac.

NATURE IN DECEMBER

Greater and lesser spotted woodpeckers thrive on the larvae hidden in tree bark. Their red flashes make a welcome splash of colour on short, grey winter days.

In mountain areas of the north, some stoats turn white in order to blend in with the snow. Occasionally the change is only partial, leaving brown 'spectacles' around the stoat's eyes.

It is easy to see rabbits in the fields now. They continue to breed through the winter, though there are fewer litters. You may see the youngsters clustering around the warren, or witness a courtship chase.

The pupae of many moths lie dormant in soil and leaf litter. When gardening you may accidentally dig up some of the red-brown pupae cases.

Decomposers on the woodland floor work hard to break down the leaf litter. The leaves of poplar, sallow, hazel, ash, elm, birch and sycamore are relatively soft and break down rapidly. But the leaves of oak, beech and sweet chestnut have a leathery texture which is more resistant to decay; this is due to the tannins which accumulate in the leaf as it ages on the tree. Tannins are the tree's defence against defoliating insects; they impair the growth and survival of caterpillars through the summer and preserve the tissues of the leaf when it has fallen.

In Britain many robins have forsaken their original woodland habitat and have become hedgerow or garden dwellers. The robin is a familiar sight in winter, as a companion to the gardener and a regular visitor to the bird table.

The Romans established the solstice as the main feast of winter by holding their week-long feast of Saturnalia during this dark, cheerless time of year. Masters waited on their servants, and the revelry was noisy and exuberant. The feast was dedicated to Saturn, an agricultural deity, and it is from Saturnalia that we have inherited our custom of exchanging gifts at midwinter, although the Church attributes its origins to Saint Nicholas.

On the night of Christmas Eve children of all ages hang up their stockings or put out their shoes, in the hope that Santa Claus (or Father Christmas) will fill them with toys and sweets.

Christmas Eve is the time to bring in the Yule log. The Yule log should never be bought, but must be found or given to you. It should be lit at dusk, using a fragment of last year's log; keep it burning all night, and if possible throughout the twelve days of Christmas. Keep a piece to light next year's log, and it will protect the house from fire.

15

16

17

18

19

20 *Saint Thomas's Eve*

21 *The Feast of Saint Thomas, the patron saint of carpenters and masons*
The winter solstice

22 *The sun enters the House of Capricorn*

23

24 *Christmas Eve*

25 *Christmas Day*

26 *Saint Stephen's Day. Saint Stephen was the first Christian martyr*
Boxing Day

27 *Saint John's Day. Saint John is the patron saint of booksellers,*
publishers, printers and writers

28 *Holy Innocents' Day or Childermas*

On Boxing Day, tradespeople, servants and children used to go 'boxing', carrying earthenware 'Christmas boxes' with a slit in the top. Householders whom they had served during the year were asked to put coins into the pots.

The Holy Innocents of this day were the children of Bethlehem, of two years old or less, who were killed by Herod in an attempt to get rid of the baby Jesus. In Spain, on Holy Innocents' Day, people play jokes on each other in much the same way as on April Fools' Day in other countries.

Trees have had a place at the time of the winter solstice since well before the Christian era. The Romans honoured the myth of the death and revival of Adonis by paying homage to a pine tree. It is said that the Celts felled a ritual tree at the time of the winter solstice and then buried it, probably as a symbol of the death of vegetation. The Christmas tree, as we know it, possibly came from Germany, where the medieval mystery plays had the Paradise Tree, decorated with apples and encircled by candles, as the central object.

'And the fir tree was put into a great tub filled with sand; but no-one could see that it was a tub, for it was hung around with green cloth, and stood on a large many-coloured carpet. Oh, how the tree trembled! What was to happen now? The servants, and the young ladies, decked it out. On one branch they hung little nets, cut out of coloured paper; every net was filled with sweets; golden apples and walnuts hung down as if they grew there, and more than a hundred little candles, red, white and blue, were fastened to the different boughs. Dolls that looked exactly like real people swung among the foliage, and high on the summit of the tree was fixed a tinsel star.'

from *The Fir Tree* by Hans Christian Andersen

In the old days in Sweden, it was traditional to race home from church, in the early hours of Christmas morning, in sleds or horse-drawn wagons. The first person home was believed to have the best harvest in the coming year.

'In the cold north men eat bread of fir bark; in our own fields the mouse, if pressed for food in the winter, will gnaw the bark of sapling trees. Frost sharpens the teeth like a file, and hunger is keener than frost.'

from *The Field Play* by Richard Jefferies

29	**DECEMBER**
30	
31 *New Year's Eve, or Hogmanay*	

Be sure to finish any task you have in hand today, for if the task is carried into the New Year it will not prosper.

Light your evening meal on Christmas Eve with a red candle; it should be big enough to light the evening meal on each of the twelve days of Christmas.

At midnight on Hogmanay, Scots welcome the first visitor of the New Year. This 'first-footer' should be a tall, dark-haired man bearing gifts of bread, whisky, a piece of coal and a silver coin. The man should enter the house in silence, and no-one must speak to him until he has put the coal on the fire, poured a glass of whisky and wished everyone a 'Happy New Year'.

At the end of the month of February there is a picture of a hawthorn bush, sheltering 37 animals. The sketch above identifies them all:

1 bumble bee
2 solitary bee
3 common flower bug
4 kestrel with mouse
5 blackbird
6 hover fly
7 crab spider
8 sawfly larva
9 lackey moth
10 lackey moth larva

11 honey bee
12 sawfly
13 small ermine larvae
14 blue tit
15 winter moth larva
16 common capsid bug
17 magpie stealing egg
18 chaffinch nest
19 greenfly
20 mirid bug

21 dunnock nest
22 snipe-fly
23 seven-spot ladybird
24 orb web spider
25 great tit
26 early moth and larva
27 small eggar moth
28 leaf beetle
29 male and female
   winter moth

30 hawthorn shield bug
31 snail
32 wood mouse
33 leaf hopper
34 slug
35 dunnock with
   crane-fly
36 hedgehog
37 bank vole

At the beginning of the month of July there is a seashore scene with 20 animals and plants to identify:

1 common tern
2 common gull
3 little gull
4 puffins
5 kittiwake
6 oyster-catcher
7 knots
8 ringed plover

9 the shells include:
   trough shells, tellins,
   periwinkles
10 long-horned poppy
11 sea spurrey
12 sea holly
13 sea campion
14 rock samphire

15 common scurvygrass
16 thrift
17 red admiral butterfly
18 sea aster
19 sea bindweed
20 burnet rose

Mari Friend

This daybook reflects Mari Friend's love of nature, her deep knowledge and understanding of the lore of plants and animals, and of folklore. Her text and the quotations she has chosen provide an insight into some of the festivals and special days that were – and in many cases still are – celebrated in the western world. Her nature notes follow the change of seasons and complement her gloriously detailed illustrations which record the wonders and intricacies of the natural world. These illustrations are taken from her book, *Small Wonder – A New Approach to Understanding Nature*, with a foreword by David Bellamy, which was published in 1991 by Blandford Press.

Born and brought up in the north of England, Mari Friend studied botany, biology and horticulture. She has run a popular countryside centre outside Bradford, designed gardens, and taken part in several radio and television programmes.

Mari Friend lives among the rugged beauty of the Peak District of Derbyshire where she writes and draws, also devoting much time to the care of the extraordinary wildlife garden she created in a small medieval field at the back of her cottage.